T5-ANA-302

Dear Parents,

Are you aware that students can lose up to 25% of their reading and math skills during the summer break*? While the freedom away from school during the summer can be a wonderful time in your child's life, the reality is children will experience summer learning loss if they don't practice the skills they developed during the school year. That is why we created Summer Vacation®, a valuable investment in your child's future. Summer Vacation is a fun, entertaining educational program designed to help your child review skills learned during the previous school year and prepare for the challenges of the next.

This 1st grade activity workbook has been thoroughly reviewed and recommended by an esteemed panel of teachers. It is packed with fun, skills-based activities for every day of the summer. Some of the activities in this book include:

- New 12-chapter story and fun reading comprehension activities
- New progressive project – "Create your own Calendar"
- New fun stickers to track progress
- Counting exercises
- Basic addition
- Pattern recognition and identification
- Scavenger hunts of objects around your house
- Drawing, arts and crafts activities
- Simple telling time exercises

We suggest that you work with your child to complete many of the activities in this workbook, since reading skills have likely not been mastered at this stage in your child's development. It may be beneficial to pick a certain time each day to work on the activities. This consistency will help make participation a habit, and will provide some quality time that will ultimately assist with your child's educational development.

We hope you and your child enjoy Summer Vacation®!

*Source: Harris Cooper, professor and chairman of the psychology department at the University of Missouri at Columbia.

Summer Vacation® Teacher Review Panel

Our panel of distinguished educators was instrumental in ensuring that the Summer Vacation® program offers your child maximum educational benefit. This panel provided key ideas and feedback on all aspects of our workbook series. We welcome your feedback.

Please contact us at:
Attn: Summer Vacation, Entertainment Publications, 2125 Butterfield Road, Troy, Michigan 48084
or e-mail us at
summervacation@entertainment.com.

Cathy Cerveny, Baltimore, MD
Maryland Teacher of the Year, 1996
Fifth-grade teacher; Integrated
Language Arts curriculum writer
Served on Maryland's Professional
Standards and Teacher Education Board

Norma Jackson, Keller, TX
Texas Teacher of the Year, 1999
On special assignment as District Writing
Specialist for grades K–5
Second-grade teacher
Summer Activity Writing Specialist

Becky Miller, Mason, OH
Gifted Coordinator for Mason City Schools
Taught elementary grades 3 and 4
Adjunct Professor at
Xavier University

Laurie Sybert, Lake Ozark, MO
Missouri Teacher of the Year, 1999
Second-grade teacher
Elementary Science coordinator
Fulbright Teacher Scholar

Jenlane Gee Matt, Modesto, CA
California Teacher of the Year, 1988
National Teacher of the Year finalist, 1989
Third-grade teacher

Gemma Hoskins, Bel Air, MD
Maryland Teacher of the Year, 1992
Technology Coordinator for school
Former fifth-grade teacher and
elementary teacher specialist

Charles Mercer, Washington, DC
District of Columbia Teacher of the Year, 1999
Worked at NASA's Education Program Office
Elementary Science resource
teacher, PK–6

Denise Johnson, New York, NY
Teacher Center Specialist in Manhattan
Previously taught grades 4–8
Instructor at Brooklyn College

**Richard Scott Griffin,
Mount Holly, NC**
North Carolina Teacher of the Year, 1996
Teaches grades 4-6—all subject areas
Served as Teacher Advisor to State Board
of Education

Rob O'Leary, Sidney, OH
School principal
Former fourth-grade teacher
Fellowship Award recipient from
Wright State University

Bruce Fisher, Arcata, CA
California Teacher of the Year, 1991
Teacher for 23 years at
Fortuna Elementary
Distinguished Teacher in Residence
at Humboldt State University

Getting Ready
for
First Grade

In kindergarten, your child got a good start on reading and writing skills by getting to know the connections among letters, sounds and words. Your kindergarten graduate may be able to:

- recite the letters and sounds of the alphabet.
- make connections between spoken words and printed letters.
- read simple words such as *the, and, it* and *is.*
- write his or her name and a few simple words using phonetic spelling.
- print letters and numbers with some proficiency.
- use letters and sounds he or she knows to start writing things such as lists and invitations.
- recite his or her age, address and phone number.
- count to 30 or higher.

Grade 1 Skills

First grade will be an exciting year as your child starts to become an independent reader and writer. By the end of first grade, your child may be able to:

- read at least 100 words.
- locate the main idea in stories.
- remember the sequence of events in stories.
- print words legibly.
- capitalize the first word in a sentence.
- use a period or a question mark at the end of a sentence.
- recognize the singular and plural forms of nouns.
- use phonetic skills to "sound out" words.
- correctly spell some simple words.
- count to 100 in increments of 1, 2, 5 and 10.
- write numerals to 100.
- add and subtract numbers up to 10.
- understand the place value for two-digit numbers.

How You Can Help

You can help prepare your child for first grade by making this Summer Vacation® workbook a regular part of your daily routine. Read the stories together, help your child with the written activities, and complete the calendar project. The Summer Vacation workbook is designed to help your child retain the skills that he or she developed in kindergarten and to prepare him or her for the challenges of first grade.

Party at Laughing Lake

Chapter 1: The Welcome Home Party

Ask an adult to help you read this story.

Reggie is a raccoon. He is always looking for something to do. Reggie likes to have fun.

Diggs is a dog. He is Reggie's friend. He likes to have fun, too.

Reggie and Diggs live by a lake. It is summer, and it is hot.

"There is nothing to do," said Diggs.

Activity 1

Skill: Classifying—Same/Different Words

Circle the picture that is different.

Reggie said, "Oh, yes, there is. We must plan a party."

"What for?" asked Diggs.

"The Dragonfly family comes back to the lake today," said Reggie. "They have been in the South all winter. It is warm there."

"We will welcome them," said Diggs.

Activity 2

Skill: Reading Comprehension—Setting

Circle the picture that shows what kind of day it is.

BEACH crossword

Across ➡

1.

2.

Down ⬇

1.

2.

3.

4.

HINTS: fan   starfish   ball   sand   shell   wave

HIDDEN OBJECTS

Look for these objects hiding in the picture. Color each object you find!

POST OFFICE

7

Count the items around your house and fill in the blanks.

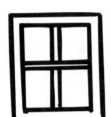 My home has _____ **windows.**

There are _____ **pictures** in my home.

I can count _____ **light switches** in my home.

Draw a line to the time of day you do each activity shown below.

 10:00PM

 4:00PM

 7:00AM

Getting up

Sleeping

Playing Soccer

What Doesn't Belong?

Draw an X on the picture that doesn't belong.

Make a Calendar:
Adult supervision is recommended.

September

Introduction to the Project

During the next 12 weeks, your child has the opportunity to make a personalized calendar. This project will help your child have a better concept of time as he or she enters first grade. As children create their own calendars, they will review days of the week, months of the year, and numbers up to 31. Small motor skills will develop as your child uses crayons, scissors, and glue.

Children should be supervised during the making of the calendar to ensure safety while using scissors or glue. Templates, or patterns, are provided to help create many of the calendar crafts. A template of the calendar grid is also provided. Photocopy the grid below to use for each calendar month. The calendar begins with September to build anticipation for the coming school year.

Sunday	Monday	Tuesday	Wednesday	Thursday	Friday	Saturday

Master Materials List (Items you will need for all 12 weeks of the project.)

scissors
nontoxic glue suitable
   for paper
package of different-colored
   construction paper
pencil
crayons
old magazines
4 or 5 brown pipe cleaners
ruler

red, yellow, and orange
   buttons
2 8-in. (20.3-cm) paper plates
hole punch
several strands of brown,
   orange and white yarn
cotton balls
sheet of white paper
clip-type clothespin
small, sealable plastic bag

scraps of wrapping paper or
   tissue paper
plastic straw
tape
nontoxic washable paint
paper towels
washable markers
paintbrush or sponge cut
   into pieces
watermelon seeds (optional)
stapler (optional)

Materials

scissors

glue

construction paper

pencil

red crayon

old magazines

> **September is the ninth month of the year. It has 30 days. Fall begins. Children go back to school.**

Directions

1. Cut out a copy of the calendar grid. Glue the grid to a sheet of construction paper.

2. Ask an adult what day of the week September starts on this year.

3. Number the squares from 1 to 30. Write the name of the month above the calendar grid.

4. Some calendars show holidays or special days in red. These are some holidays you might want to put on your calendar. Circle the date with a red crayon. If anyone in your family has a birthday in September, add it to your red-letter days.

Labor Day	The first Monday in September
Fall begins	September 23
Rosh Hashanah, Yom Kippur	Ask an adult what days of the week these holidays fall on this year.
Birthdays and Special Events_____	

5. What will you need to start school? Cut pictures from a magazine of things you will have in your backpack. Glue your pictures to the construction paper.

Can you find...?

Circle the items hidden in the picture.

Reggie

Diggs

Tree

Summer Vacation® Book

Food Dish

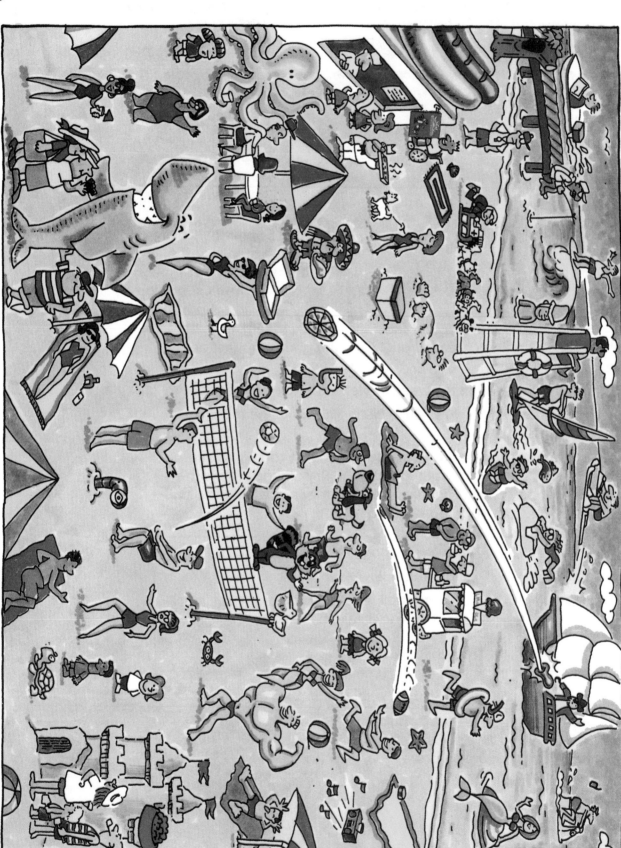

Friday

Add the groups together.

 + =

1. _____ _____ _____

 + =

2. _____ _____ _____

 + =

3. _____ _____ _____

+ =

4. _____ _____ _____

Circle the pattern that is different.

1.

2.

3.

4.

13

Draw a line to the picture that starts with the letter.

R

I

F

Maze

START

FINISH

ACTIVITY

Adult supervision is recommended.

Stuffed Paper Bag Owl

Materials:

2 brown lunch bags

1 to 2 sheets of
 newspaper

yarn or string

scissors

glue

construction paper:
 brown, orange,
 yellow, black,
 and white

Directions:

1. Crumple up the newspaper sheets. Place them inside one of the bags.

2. Open and place the other bag on top of the stuffed bag and push it down until it covers the stuffed bag.

3. Tie yarn or string around the bags to make the owl's head and body.

4. Cut out a white heart and glue it on the owl's head.

5. Cut out black and yellow circles for eyes. Make the black circles smaller than the yellow circles. Make a yellow triangle for the beak. Glue them on the head.

6. Cut out big brown wings. Glue them to the sides of the body.

7. Cut small orange, yellow, brown, and white rectangles.

8. Glue them in overlapping rows to the owl's chest for a feathered look.

ACTIVITY

Adult supervision is recommended.

Newspaper Lion

Directions:

1. Put two sheets of newspaper on top of one another.

2. Draw and cut out a large circle from the newspaper.

3. Glue the circles together but leave an opening big enough for a hand.

4. Let this dry.

5. Crumple up a sheet of newspaper and stuff it in the circles.

6. Now glue the opening shut.

7. Cut a few 2-inch (5 cm) strips of crepe paper.

8. Gather and glue them around the whole circle.

9. Cut out a heart from construction paper. Glue it on the circle as shown to form the lion's face.

10. Now cut out other parts of the face from construction paper and glue them in place.

Materials:

newspaper

scissors

glue

crepe paper—
 brown or yellow

construction paper

pencil

COMPLETE THE KIDS

Draw the hair on the boy and girl.
Use our ideas or design your own.

Party at Laughing Lake

Chapter 2: Party Plans

Ask an adult to help you read this story.

Diggs asked, "What do we need for a party?"

"We need food," said Reggie.

"We need music," said Diggs.

"We need presents," said Reggie.

"We need balloons," said Diggs.

Activity 1

Skill: Make Connections

Match each animal to its house.

Then Reggie asked, "Where can we have the party?"

Diggs and Reggie thought and thought.

At last Reggie said, "We can have it at the lake."

Diggs said, "We will ask Woody Beaver. He lives by the lake."

Activity 2

Skill: Rhyming Words

Circle the picture of the word that sounds like *house*.

AMUSEMENT PARK crossword

Across ➡

1.

2.

Down ⬇

1.

2.

HINTS: cars   candy   rides   games

HIDDEN OBJECTS

L👀k for these objects hiding in the picture. Color each object you find!

COLOR ME!

SCAVENGER COUNTING

Count the items around your house and fill in the blanks.

My home has _____ **clocks.**

There are _____ **tables** in my home.

I can count _____ **lamps** in my home.

Draw a line to the time of day you do each activity shown below.

8:00PM   12:00PM   3:00PM

Getting off the bus   Bedtime story   Eating lunch

What Doesn't Belong?

Draw an X on the picture that doesn't belong.

Make a Calendar:

Adult supervision is recommended.

October

Materials

scissors
glue or tape
construction paper
pencil
red crayon
3 or 4 brown pipe cleaners
red, yellow, and orange buttons

October is the tenth month of the year. Halloween comes at the end of the month. Some people have campfires and roast marshmallows or hot dogs.

Directions

1. Cut out a copy of the calendar grid. Glue the grid to a sheet of construction paper.

2. Ask an adult what day of the week October starts on this year.

3. Number the squares from 1 to 31.

4. Write the month above the calendar grid.

5. Some calendars show holidays in red. These are some holidays you might want to put on your calendar. Circle the date with a red crayon. If anyone in your family has a birthday in October, add it to your red-letter days.

Columbus Day	The second Monday in October
Thanksgiving Day (Canada)	The second Monday in October
Halloween	October 31
Birthdays and Special Events	_____
	_____
	_____
	_____

6. Decorate the top of your calendar. You might choose to make an autumn tree.

7. Fold three or four brown pipe cleaners in half, and twist them together. See **Figure 1**.

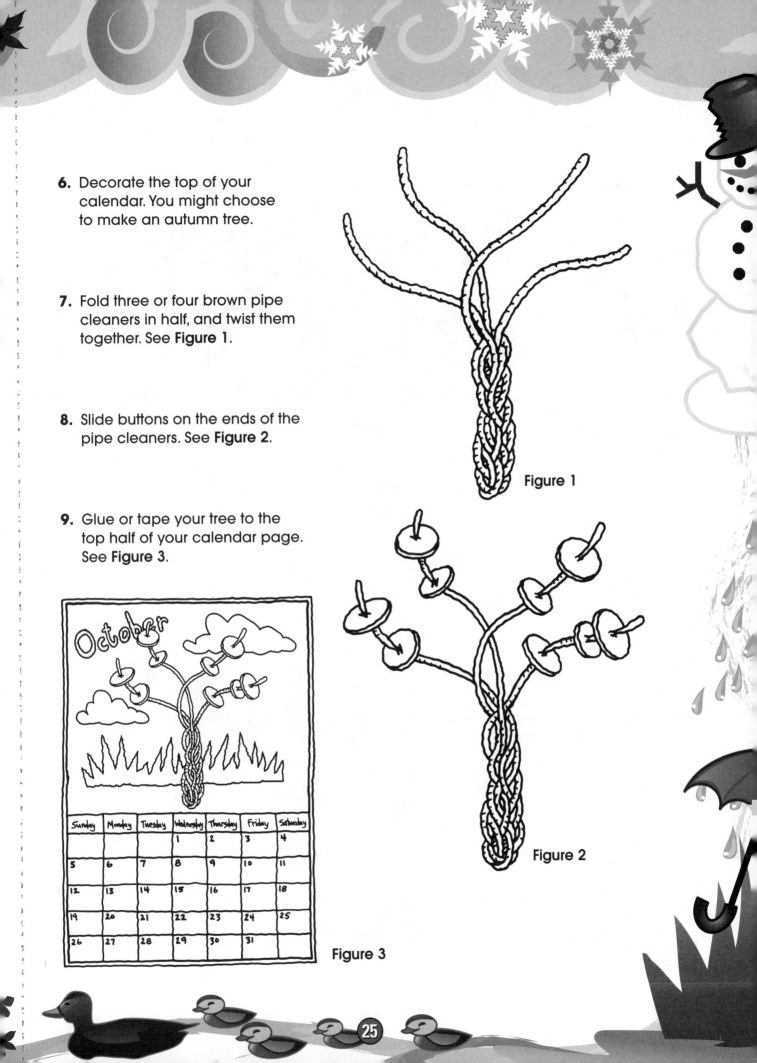

Figure 1

8. Slide buttons on the ends of the pipe cleaners. See **Figure 2**.

9. Glue or tape your tree to the top half of your calendar page. See **Figure 3**.

Figure 2

Figure 3

Sunday	Monday	Tuesday	Wednesday	Thursday	Friday	Saturday
			1	2	3	4
5	6	7	8	9	10	11
12	13	14	15	16	17	18
19	20	21	22	23	24	25
26	27	28	29	30	31	

October

Can you find...?

Circle the items hidden in the picture.

Reggie

Diggs

Tree

Summer
Vacation®
Book

Food Dish

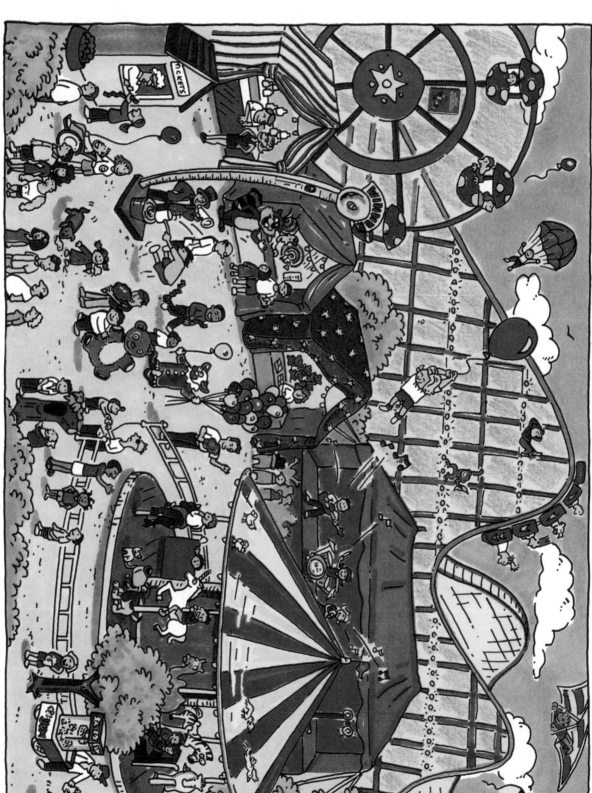

Friday

Search for Answers

Look at the picture on page 26 and use the word list to fill in the blanks in the sentences below. *Have an adult help you!*

purple   banana

birds   yellow

Diggs   three

dart board   balloons

tickets

1. _____ is standing next to a cat on the merry-go-round.

2. The monkey hanging from the roller coaster is holding a _____.

3. The colors of the ferris wheel cars are _____ and _____.

4. There are _____ people riding on the ferris wheel.

5. You can buy _____ at the booth next to Diggs' Food Dish.

6. There are four _____ on top of the merry-go-round.

7. The clown is handing out _____.

8. There is a _____ in the game tent next to Reggie.

MATCHING SOUNDS

Draw a line to the picture that starts with the letter.

K

A

D

Maze

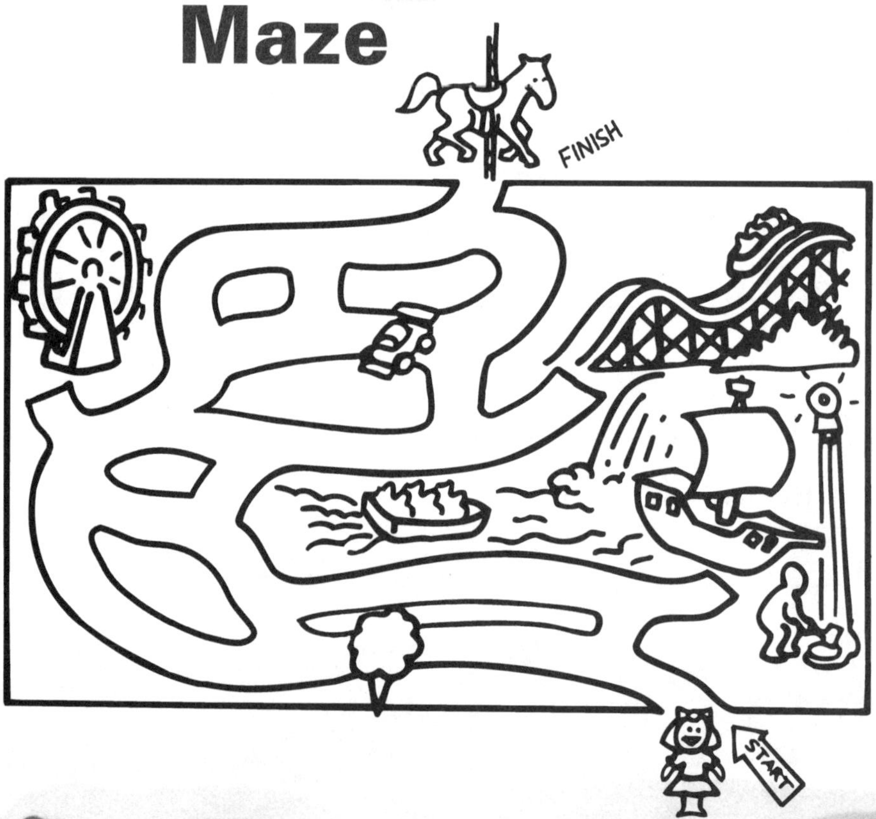

COLOR ME!

FINISH

START

ACTIVITY

Adult supervision is recommended.

Big Ladybug

Materials:

construction
  paper—yellow,
  red, black, white

scissors

glue

black marker

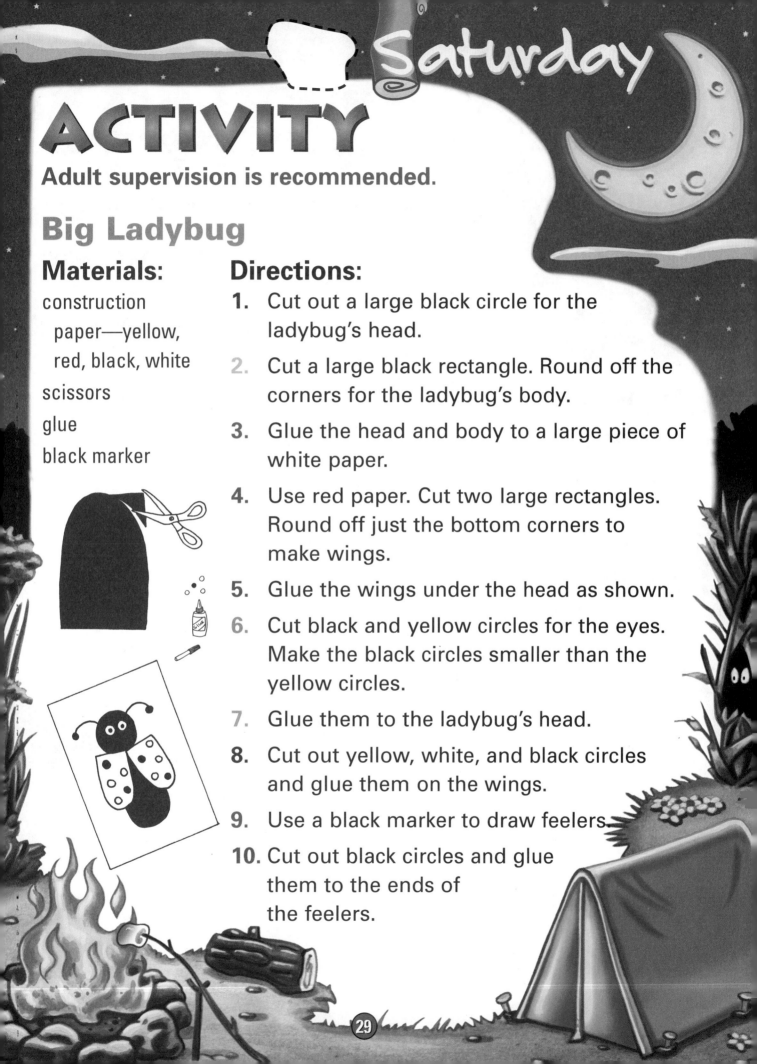

Directions:

1. Cut out a large black circle for the ladybug's head.

2. Cut a large black rectangle. Round off the corners for the ladybug's body.

3. Glue the head and body to a large piece of white paper.

4. Use red paper. Cut two large rectangles. Round off just the bottom corners to make wings.

5. Glue the wings under the head as shown.

6. Cut black and yellow circles for the eyes. Make the black circles smaller than the yellow circles.

7. Glue them to the ladybug's head.

8. Cut out yellow, white, and black circles and glue them on the wings.

9. Use a black marker to draw feelers.

10. Cut out black circles and glue them to the ends of the feelers.

ACTIVITY

Adult supervision is recommended.

Picture Stretch

Directions:

1. Cut the front cover of an old greeting card into strips.

2. Arrange the strips in order on a piece of construction paper. Leave a little space between each one.

3. Glue the strips in place.

Materials:

construction paper

old greeting card

scissors

glue

COMPLETE THE KIDS

Draw the eyes on the kids.
Use our ideas or create your own.

Party at Laughing Lake

Chapter 3: The Singing Ducks

Ask an adult to help you read this story.

On the way to Woody Beaver's house, Reggie and Diggs see Mother Duck and her four ducklings.

"Good morning, Reggie," said the ducklings.

"Will you come to our party for the Dragonfly family?" asked Reggie.

"Yes!" said all the ducklings.

Activity 1

Skill: Word Reading

Fill in the blanks with the word that tells about the picture.

Across

3.

4.

5.

Down

1.   2.

"Good!" said Reggie.

"The ducklings will sing a song for the party," said Mother Duck.

"Quack!" sang the ducklings. "Quack! Quack! Quack!"

"Very nice," said Reggie, but Diggs put his paws over his ears.

Activity 2

Skill: Reading Comprehension—Story Events

Circle the picture that shows what the ducks will do at the party.

ZOO **crossword**

Across ➡

1.

2.

Down ⬇

1.

2.

HINTS: lion   eagle   tiger   goose

HIDDEN OBJECTS

L**⊙⊙**k for these objects hiding in the picture. Color each object you find!

Wednesday
SCAVENGER COUNTING

Count the items around your house and fill in the blanks.

I can count _____ **spoons** in my kitchen.

My room has _____ **pillows**.

I can count _____ pairs of **pants** in my closet.

Draw a line to the time of day you do each activity shown below.

5:00PM

7:30AM

10:00AM

Eating breakfast

In school

Doing homework

What Doesn't Belong?

Draw an X on the picture that doesn't belong.

Make a Calendar:
Adult supervision is recommended.

November

Materials
scissors
glue
construction paper
pencil
red crayon
8-in. (20.3-cm) paper plate

> The eleventh month of the year is November. It has 30 days. The leaves fall from the trees. Many people stop to give thanks for all the good things in their lives.

Directions

1. Cut out a copy of the calendar grid. Glue the grid to a sheet of construction paper.

2. Ask an adult what day of the week November starts on this year.

3. Number the squares from 1 to 30.

4. Write the month above the calendar grid.

5. Some calendars show holidays in red. These are some holidays you might want to put on your calendar. Circle the date with a red crayon. If anyone in your family has a birthday in November, add it to your red-letter days.

Veterans' Day	November 11 (This is known as Remembrance Day in Canada.)
Thanksgiving Day (U.S.)	The fourth Thursday in November
Birthdays and Special Events	_____
	_____

6. Decorate your calendar. You can make a wreath decorated with leaves.

7. Cut out the leaf patterns on the next page. See **Figure 1**.

8. Trace your leaves on green, red, yellow, and orange construction paper. Cut out your leaves.

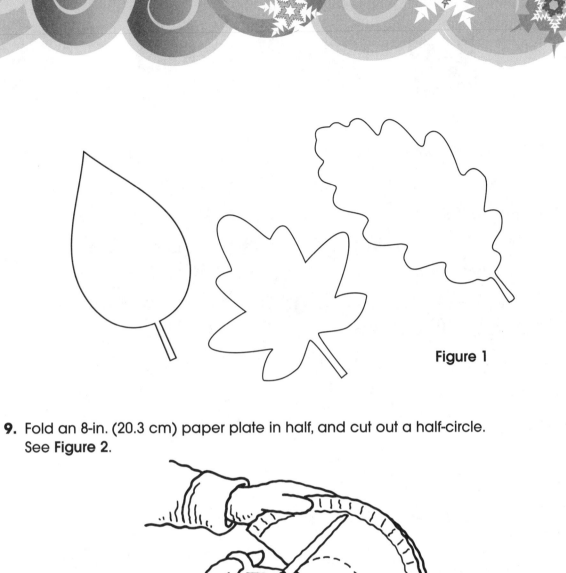

Figure 1

9. Fold an 8-in. (20.3 cm) paper plate in half, and cut out a half-circle. See **Figure 2**.

Figure 2

10. Glue your leaves to the paper ring. See **Figure 3**.

11. Glue your wreath to your calendar page.

Figure 3

Can you find...?

Circle the items hidden in the picture.

Reggie

Diggs

Tree

Summer Vacation® Book

Food Dish

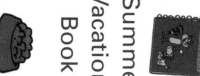

Count the Animals

Fill in the blanks with the correct number of each object.

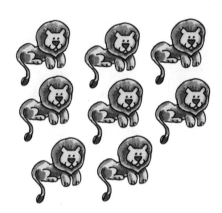

_____   _____   _____

_____   _____

_____   _____

LETTER SOUNDS

Write the first letter in each picture name.

___

___

___

___

___

___

COLOR ME!

Maze

FINISH

START

ACTIVITY

Adult supervision is recommended.

Watercolor Lantern

Materials:

watercolor paints

paintbrush

white construction
  paper

scissors

stapler

Directions:

1. Brush watercolor paint all over the white paper. Use different colors and let them blend into each other.

2. Let the painting dry.

3. Fold the paper in half longways with the painted side on the outside.

4. Cut slits 1 inch (3 cm) apart on the folded edge stopping 1 inch (3 cm) from the other edge of the paper.

5. Unfold the paper.

6. Form it into a lantern as shown and staple the edges together.

7. Cut a strip of colored paper and staple it across the top of the lantern to make a handle.

Caution: Do NOT place a candle or lightbulb in the lantern.

Sunday

ACTIVITY

Adult supervision is recommended.

Sidewalk Painter

Directions:

1. On a hot day go outside with your bucket of water and paintbrush.

2. Paint designs and pictures on the sidewalk or driveway.

3. Be sure to stand back and look at your work before it dries and disappears!

Materials:

a bucket of water
a big paintbrush

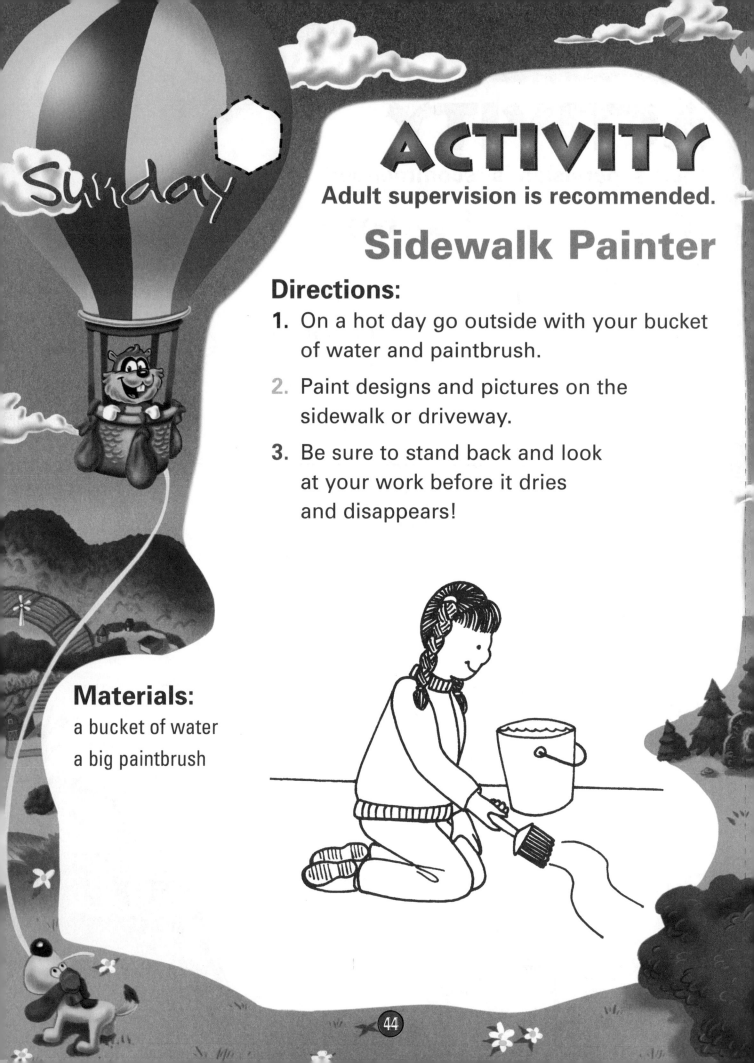

COMPLETE THE KIDS

Draw a nose on the boy and girl.
Use our ideas or design with your own.

45

Monday

Party at Laughing Lake
Chapter 4: Bee Surprised

Ask an adult to help you read this story.

Reggie and Diggs walked on to Woody Beaver's house.

Suddenly a big bee buzzed by Diggs's nose.

"Surprise!" buzzed the bee. "My name is Zippy. Who are you?"

"Surprise!" said Diggs. "My name is Diggs."

Activity 1

Skill: Phoneme Correspondence—Sound Matching

Circle the picture of the word that begins with the same beginning sound as *bee*.

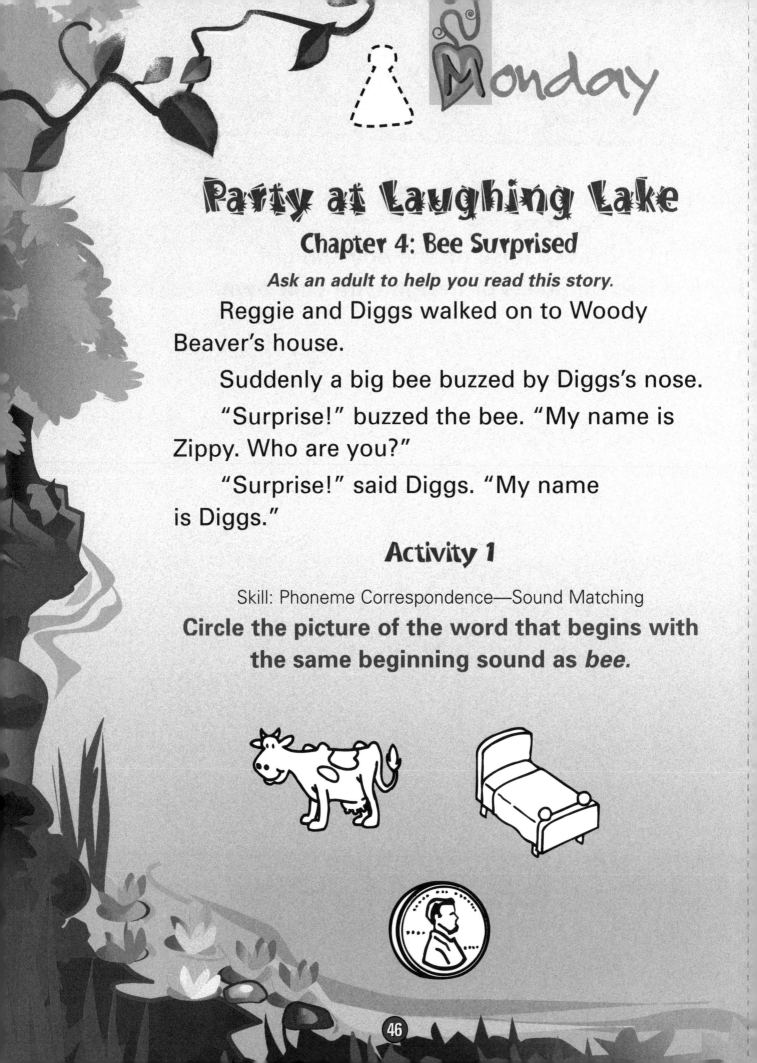

Diggs and Zippy laughed.

"Come to the Dragonfly party," said Reggie. "Bring your friends."

"We will bring honey to the party," said Zippy. "We will sing a song, too."

"Just what we need," said Diggs.

Activity 2

Skill: Reading Comprehension—Important Details

Circle the picture that shows what the bees will bring to the party.

MOVIES **crossword**

Across ➡

1.

2.

3.

Down ⬇

1.

2.

HINTS: sound screen seats candy popcorn

HIDDEN OBJECTS

L⊙⊙k for these objects hiding in the picture. Color each object you find!

Wednesday

SCAVENGER COUNTING

Count the items around your house and fill in the blanks.

I can count _____ **towels** in the bathroom.

I can count _____ **steps** in my home.

I have _____ pairs of **shoes**.

Draw a line to the time of day you do each activity shown below.

1:00PM

7:30AM

4:00PM

Riding a bike

Playing at recess

Getting dressed

What Doesn't Belong?

Draw an X on the picture that doesn't belong.

SODA

51

Make a Calendar:

Adult supervision is recommended.

Thursday
December

Materials

scissors
glue
construction paper
pencil
red crayon
hole punch
white yarn
cotton balls
crayons (optional)

December is the last month of the year. Winter comes in December. In many areas of the world, snow falls in December. It is fun to play in the snow! Be sure to dress warmly!

Directions

1. Cut out a copy of the calendar grid. Glue the grid to a sheet of construction paper.

2. Ask an adult what day of the week December starts on this year.

3. Number the squares from 1 to 31.

4. Write the month above your calendar grid.

5. Some calendars show holidays in red. These are some holidays you might want to put on your calendar. Circle the date with a red crayon. If anyone in your family has a birthday in December, add it to your red-letter days.

Hanukkah	Ask an adult what day of the week Hanukkah falls on this year.
Winter begins	December 22
Christmas Day	December 25
Boxing Day (Canada)	December 26
Kwanzaa begins	December 26
Birthdays and Special Events	_____
	_____

6. Decorate your calendar. You might want to make a pair of mittens.

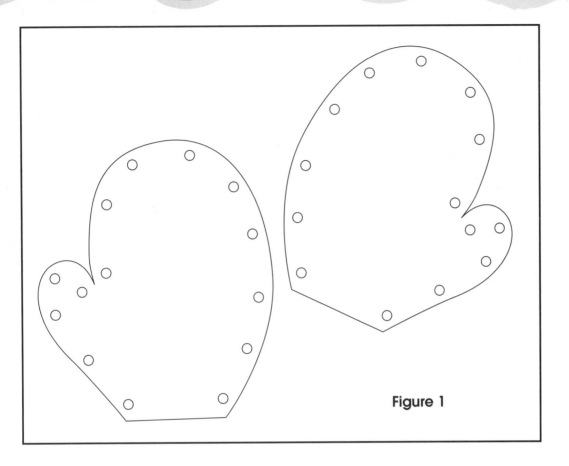

Figure 1

7. Cut out the mitten shapes on this page. See **Figure 1**. Trace two more mitten shapes on a sheet of construction paper. Cut out the shapes.

8. Piece the two mitten shapes together, and use a hole punch to make holes where the circles are.

9. You might want to use crayons to color your mittens.

10. Use a piece of yarn to lace each pair of mittens. To lace the mittens, go over, under, over, under in a pattern. See **Figure 2**. Tie the ends in knots.

11. Push cotton balls through the open end to stuff each mitten. Glue the bottom edges together.

12. Glue your mittens to your calendar page.

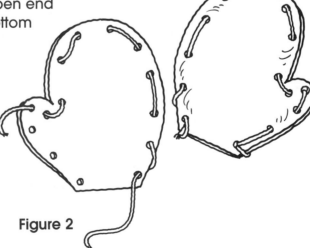

Figure 2

Can you find...? Circle the items hidden in the picture.

Reggie

Diggs

Tree

Summer Vacation® Book

Food Dish

Friday

Add the groups together.

   **+**   **=**

1. _____   _____   _____

   **+**      **=**

2. _____   _____   _____

   **+**   (food dishes)   **=**

3. _____   _____   _____

   **+**      **=**

4. _____   _____   _____

Circle the pattern that is different.

1.

2.

3.

4.

LETTER SOUNDS

Write the first letter in each picture name

_____

_____

_____

_____

_____

Maze

FINISH

START

POP CORN

COLOR ME!

ACTIVITY

Adult supervision is recommended.

Paper Bag Poncho

Materials:

large brown
  grocery bag

scissors

yarn

colored markers,
  crayons, or paint

hole punch

Directions:

1. Cut out the sides of the bag.

2. Lay the bag down flat on a table.

3. Draw a U-shaped neck opening and cut it out.

4. Decorate the front and the back with a sun, moon, and stars design or some other design that you like.

5. Punch two holes in each side of the poncho. Tie pieces of yarn in the holes.

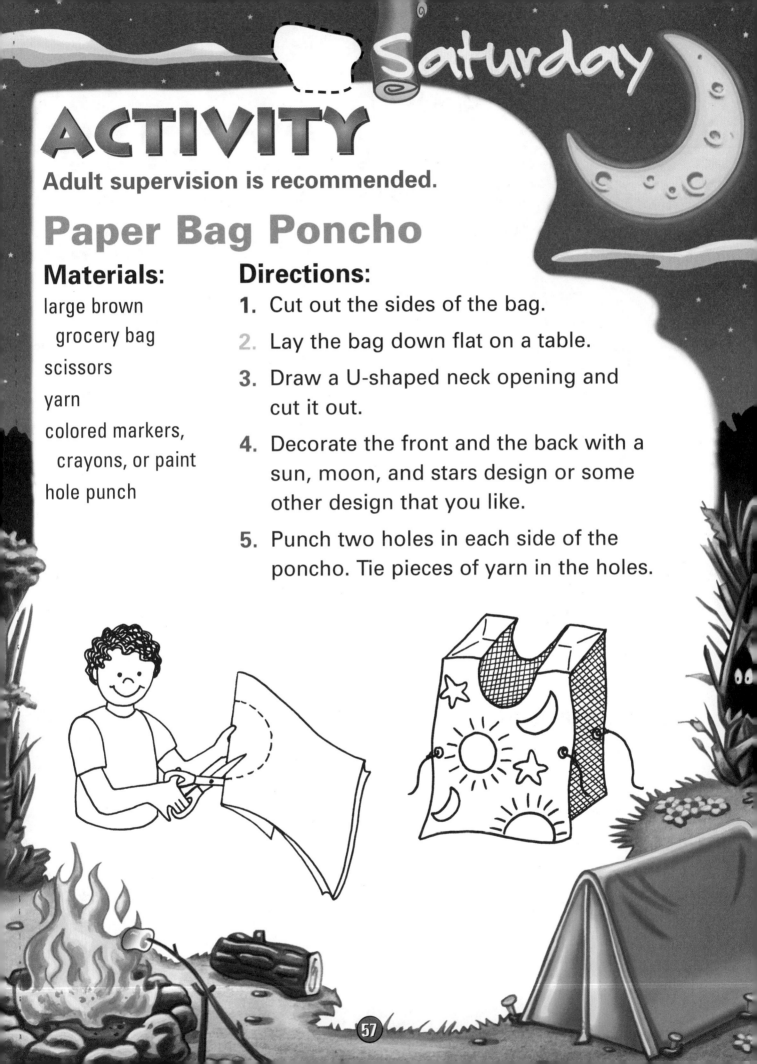

Sunday

ACTIVITY

Adult supervision is recommended.

Rainbow Sun

Directions:

1. Paint wide stripes of color across the whole piece of paper as shown. Use lots of water so that the paint is thin and easy to apply.

2. Put more water on your brush and blend the lines where the colors come together.

3. Let the painting dry completely.

4. Use a black marker. Draw a sun design over the paint.

Materials:

watercolor paints
water
wide paintbrush
white construction
  paper
black marker

Red
Orange
Yellow
Green
Blue
Purple

COMPLETE THE KIDS

Draw your favorite hat on the kids.
Use our ideas or design your own.

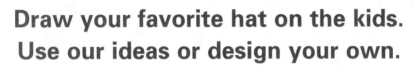

Party at Laughing Lake

Chapter 5: More Help

Ask an adult to help you read this story.

Reggie and Diggs walked up a little hill.

"Here is Velvet Rabbit," said Diggs. "Maybe she will help us plan the party."

Velvet was brushing her soft fur. "Did you say party?" she asked. "I love parties!"

"Will you help?" asked Reggie.

Activity 1

Skill: Print Awareness—Vocabulary Comprehension

Circle the picture that shows a party.

"Oh, yes!" said Velvet. "I will decorate. I love to decorate."

"Come with us to Woody Beaver's house," said Reggie.

"I will pick a special color for your party," said Velvet. "How about red?"

Activity 2

Skill: Phoneme Correspondence—Sound Matching

Circle the picture of the word that ends with the same ending sound as the word *rabbit*.

POOL

crossword

Across ➡

1.

2.

3.

Down ⬇

1.

2.

HINTS: slide   water   dive   raft   swim

HIDDEN OBJECTS

Look for these objects hiding in the picture. Color each object you find!

COLOR ME!

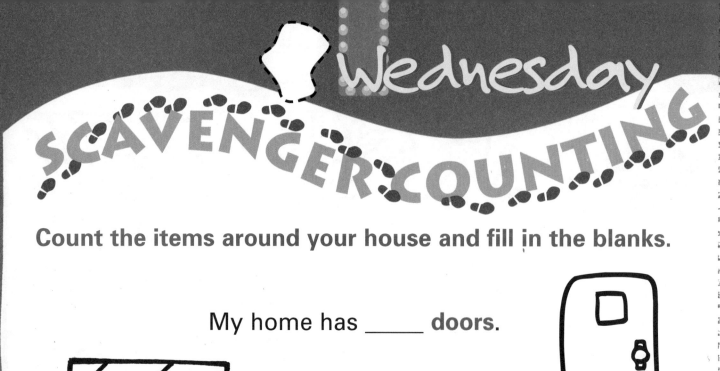

Wednesday
SCAVENGER COUNTING

Count the items around your house and fill in the blanks.

My home has _____ **doors.**

There are _____ **mirrors** in my home.

I have _____ **coats** in my closet.

Draw a line to the time of day you do each activity shown below.

11:00 PM

7:00 AM

4:00 PM

Playing with friends

Stargazing

Waking up

What Doesn't Belong?

Draw an X on the picture that doesn't belong.

Make a Calendar:
Adult supervision is recommended.

Materials
scissors
glue
construction paper
pencil
red crayon
sheet of white paper

January

January is the first month of the year. Many people have parties. Some people eat special foods on New Year's Day. There are 31 days in this month. It is cold and snowy outside in many parts of the world.

Directions

1. Cut out a copy of the calendar grid. Glue the grid to a sheet of construction paper.

2. Ask an adult what day of the week January starts on next year.

3. Number the squares from 1 to 31.

4. Write the month above your calendar grid.

5. Some calendars show holidays in red. These are some holidays you might want to put on your calendar. Circle the date with a red crayon. If anyone in your family has a birthday in January, add it to your red-letter days.

New Year's Day	January 1
Martin Luther King, Jr.'s Birthday	January 15
Birthdays and Special Events	_____
	_____
	_____
	_____
	_____

6. Decorate your calendar. You might want to make snowflakes.

7. Fold a sheet of white paper in half. Then fold it in half again.

8. Working carefully with scissors, cut out triangles or other shapes in the paper. See **Figure 1**.

Figure 1

9. When you unfold the paper, you will see a snowflake. See **Figure 2**. Repeat steps 7 and 8 if you want to make more snowflakes.

10. Glue your snowflakes to your calendar page.

Figure 2

Can you find...? Circle the items hidden in the picture.

Reggie

Diggs

Tree

Summer Vacation® Book

Food Dish

Search for Answers

Look at the picture on page 68 and use the word list to fill in the blanks in the sentences below. *Have an adult help you!*

shallow   fish
squirting   three
four   fence
radio   yellow
shivering

1. How many lifeguards are there? _____

2. What jumped out of the bucket and into the pool? _____

3. The Summer Vacation® book is found next to a _____.

4. The slide is the color _____ and empties into the _____ side of the pool.

5. The man with the garden hose is _____ the boy on the other side of the pool.

6. How many ducks are in the pool?_____

7. Reggie is standing near a white _____.

8. The boy sitting on the edge of the pool next to the lifeguard is _____ from the cold.

Draw a line to the picture that starts with the letter.

W

H

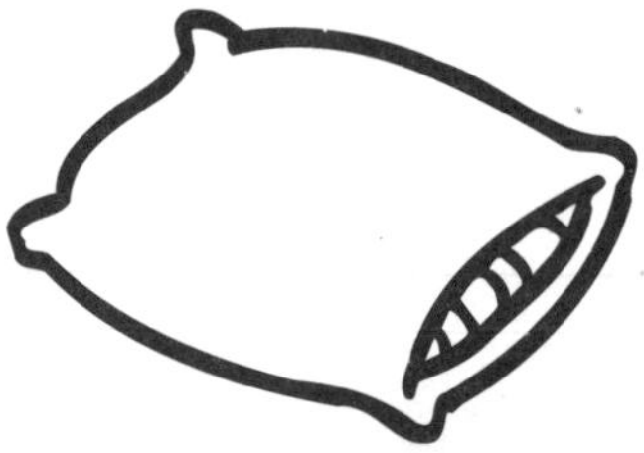

P

Maze

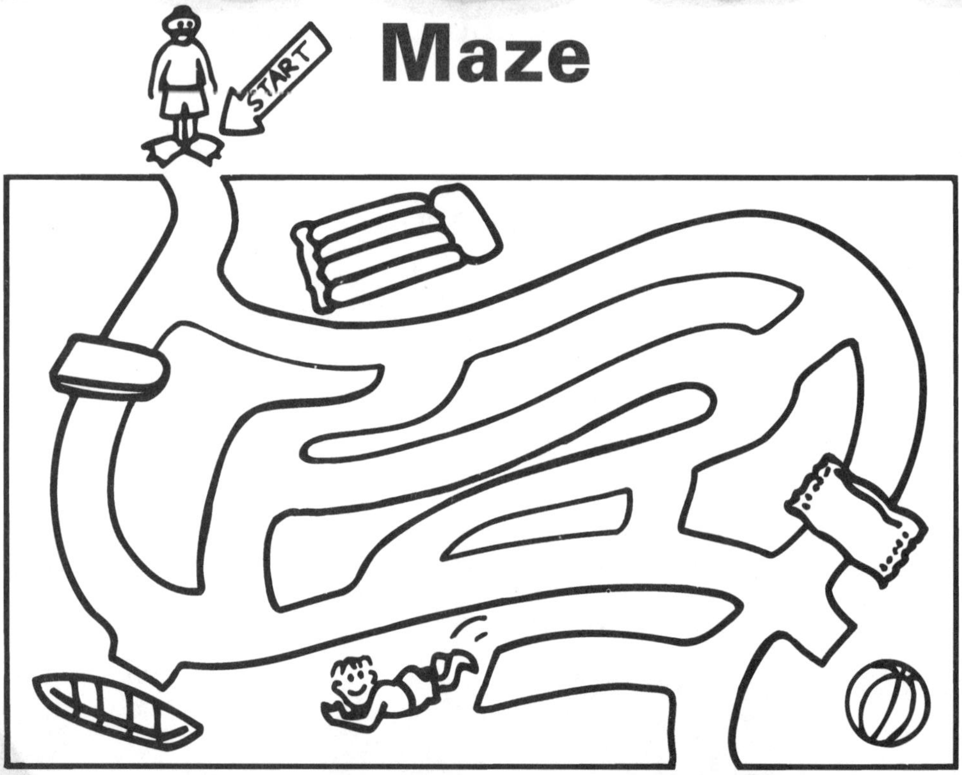

START

COLOR ME!

FINISH

ACTIVITY

Adult supervision is recommended.

Paper Plate Taco

Materials:

white paper plate
   (thin, not heavy-
   duty)

crayons

green tissue paper

construction paper
   scraps—brown,
   red, yellow

glue

scissors

Directions:

1. Color the front and the back of the paper plate brown and yellow. Color it lightly and add a few black specks to make the plate look like a tortilla.

2. Fold the paper plate in half and then open it up and lay it flat.

3. Cut two brown rectangles. Cut around the rectangles to give them a curved shaped. These will be the taco meat.

4. Glue the meat shapes to the edge of the paper plate as shown.

5. To make lettuce, shred green tissue paper and glue it to the edge of the paper plate. (Make your own shredded tissue or use gift-package stuffing.)

6. Cut a few squares of red paper and a few long, thin rectangles of yellow paper. These will become tomatoes and shredded cheese.

7. Glue the tomatoes and cheese on top of the tissue-paper lettuce.

8. Fold and glue the paper plate together.

Sunday

ACTIVITY

Adult supervision is recommended.

Rolling Art

Directions:

1. Be sure the can is empty and clean.
2. Pour some glue into a plastic bowl.
3. Cut a 12-inch (30 cm) piece of yarn.
4. Dip the whole length of the yarn into the glue.
5. Then wrap the yarn around the can in an interesting design.
6. Let the yarn dry all the way.
7. Glue two pieces of white construction paper together to make a long strip.
8. Pour a small amount of paint on a paper plate.
9. Roll the can in the paint.
10. Now roll the can down the length of your paper. Roll another row of color if you need to in order to cover the whole paper.

For more fun:

Add more color to your painting.
Make two more cans with yarn.
Use different colors of paint and roll them over the first color.

Materials:

empty metal can
yarn
scissors
glue
tempera or acrylic
  paint
paper plate
plastic bowl
white construction
            paper

COMPLETE THE KIDS

Finish dressing the kids.
Use our ideas or design your own.

73

Party at Laughing Lake
Chapter 6: Party Food

Ask an adult to help you read this story.

Diggs said, "We need food for the party."

"We need apples," said Reggie.

"We need cake," said Velvet.

"We need ice cream," said Diggs.

"We need pies," said Reggie.

Activity 1

Skill: Reading Comprehension—Relate Text with Prior Knowledge

Circle the picture of something you would eat at a party.

Diggs said, "Frankie Frog can help us. He makes yummy mud pies."

"We do not want mud pies," said Velvet. "We want berry pies."

"We want 'berry good' pies," Reggie laughed.

Activity 2

Skill: Word Classification—Identify Verbs

A verb is a word that tells an action. *Run* is a verb. It tells an action.

Circle the word below that tells an action.

red   pretty

sing

PLANETARIUM crossword

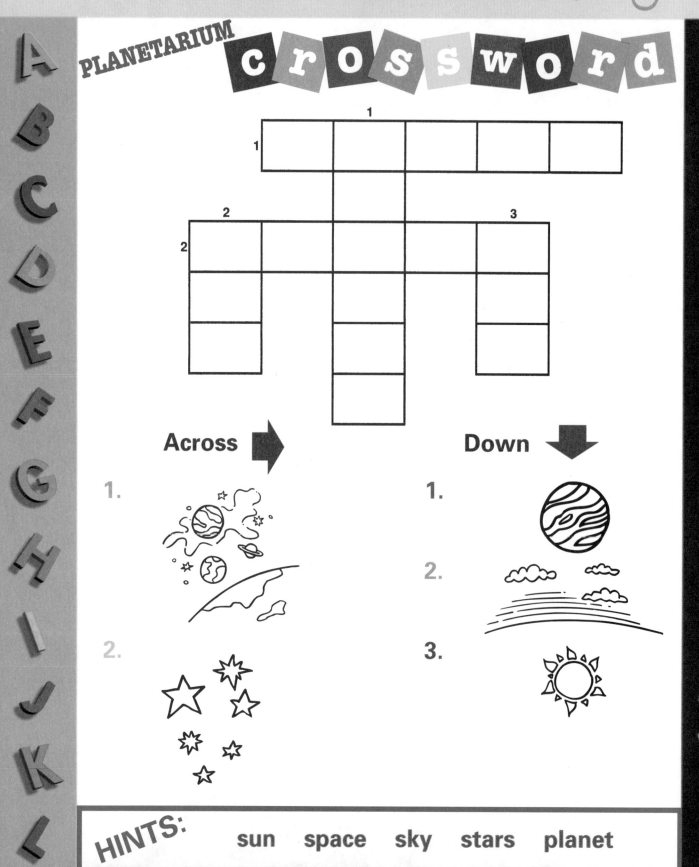

Across ➡

1.

2.

Down ⬇

1.

2.

3.

HINTS: sun   space   sky   stars   planet

HIDDEN OBJECTS

L👀k for these objects hiding in the picture. Color each object you find!

SCAVENGER COUNTING

Count the items around your house and fill in the blanks.

I have _____ **hats.**

I can count _____ **belts** in my room.

I am wearing _____ **zippers.**

Draw a line to the time of day you do each activity shown below.

 7:00PM

 8:00AM

 1:00PM

Getting on the bus

Playing at recess

Taking a bath

What Doesn't Belong?

Draw an X on the picture that doesn't belong.

Make a Calendar:
Adult supervision is recommended.

February

Materials
scissors
glue
construction paper
pencil
red crayon

The second month is February. It is the month with the fewest days. Once every four years, an extra day is added to February. A year with an extra day is called Leap Year. People send cards, flowers, or candy to those they love on Valentine's Day.

Directions

1. Cut out a copy of the calendar grid. Glue the grid to a sheet of construction paper.

2. Ask an adult what day of the week February starts on next year.

3. Number the squares from 1 to 28. If it's a Leap Year, number the squares from 1 to 29.

4. Write the month above the calendar grid.

5. Some calendars show holidays in red. These are some holidays you might want to put on your calendar. Use a red crayon to circle the date. If anyone in your family has a birthday in February, add it to your red-letter days.

Groundhog Day	February 2
Lincoln's Birthday	February 12
St. Valentine's Day	February 14
Washington's Birthday	February 22
Presidents' Day	The third Monday in February

Birthdays and Special Events _____

_____

_____

_____

6. Decorate your calendar. You may wish to make people or animals from hearts.

7. Fold a sheet of red or pink construction paper in half.

8. Working carefully with scissors, cut out half-heart shapes in the paper. Unfold the shapes to see your hearts.

9. Glue the hearts onto the page, using one heart for the body and another for the head. You can also use smaller hearts for legs and a tail.

Reggie

Diggs

Tree

Summer
Vacation®
Book

Food Dish

Object Count
How many objects can you count?
Fill in the blanks with the correct number of each object.

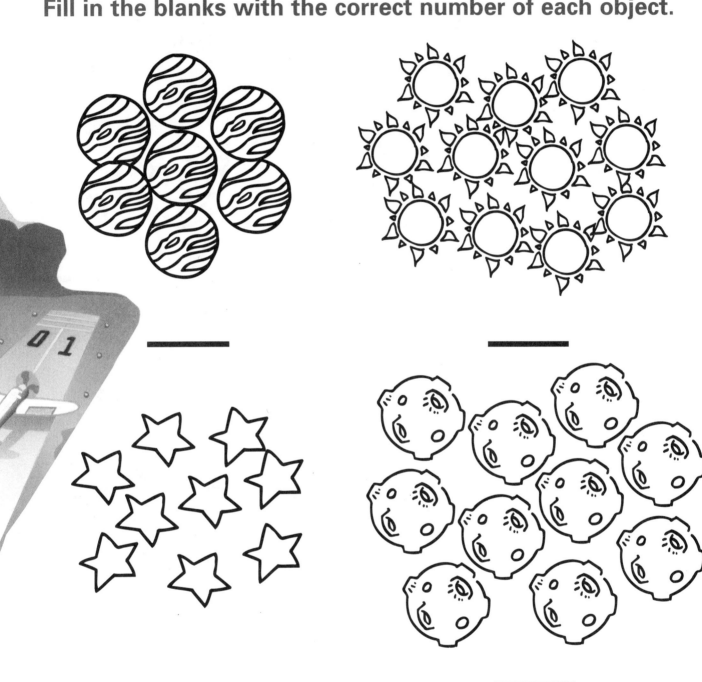

LETTER SOUNDS

_____   _____

_____   _____   _____

Maze

COLOR ME!

START

FINISH

84

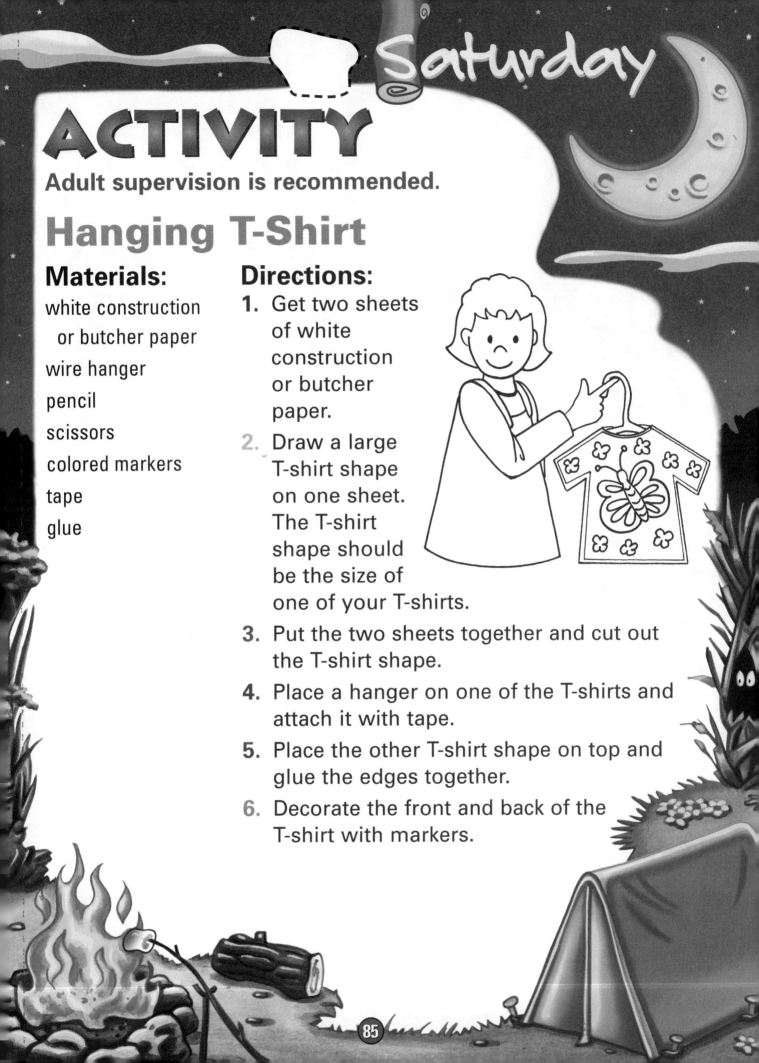

Saturday

ACTIVITY

Adult supervision is recommended.

Hanging T-Shirt

Materials:

white construction
  or butcher paper

wire hanger

pencil

scissors

colored markers

tape

glue

Directions:

1. Get two sheets of white construction or butcher paper.

2. Draw a large T-shirt shape on one sheet. The T-shirt shape should be the size of one of your T-shirts.

3. Put the two sheets together and cut out the T-shirt shape.

4. Place a hanger on one of the T-shirts and attach it with tape.

5. Place the other T-shirt shape on top and glue the edges together.

6. Decorate the front and back of the T-shirt with markers.

ACTIVITY

Adult supervision is recommended.

Quick Basket

Directions:

1. Fold a 12"x 18" (31 cm x 46 cm) piece of white construction paper in half lengthwise.

2. Glue the long edges together. Leave the short ends unglued. Let the paper dry.

3. Decorate the front and the back of the paper.

4. Now fold the paper in half widthwise.

5. Hold it by the two inside edges that come together. Staple those two edges together so that a two-sided container is formed.

6. Cut a 1-inch (3 cm) strip of construction paper for a handle.

7. Staple the handle as shown.

8. Tuck flowers or treats in the basket and give it to someone.

Materials:

white construction
  paper

glue

stapler

scissors

crayons or colored
  markers

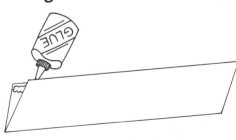

COMPLETE THE KIDS

Draw a shirt on the girl and boy. Use our ideas or design your own. If you need to, draw the arms.

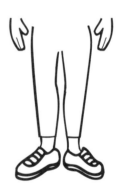

Party at Laughing Lake

Chapter 7: A Little Lake Music

Ask an adult to help you read this story.

They went to see Frankie Frog. He sat in the mud. He took a big breath. Then he said, "Ribbet!"

Another frog called, "Ribbet!"

"Do you have any pies?" asked Reggie. "We need pies for our party."

Activity 1

Skill: Phoneme Correspondence—Match Beginning Sounds

Circle the picture of the word that begins with the same beginning sound as the word *fan*.

"Ribbet!" said Frankie. "No pies."

"Ribbet! Ribbet!" called the other frogs. "No pies!"

"We cannot bring pies to the party," said Frankie. "But we will bring our songs."

"Ribbet! Ribbet!" sang the frogs.

Activity 2

Skill: Story Comprehension—Main Idea and Details

Circle the picture that does not belong at the Dragonfly party.

CIRCUS crossword

Across ➡

1. 🦁🦁

2. ⛺

3. 🐕🐕

Down ⬇

1. 🤡

2. 🐯

HINTS: tiger   lions   clown   tent   dogs

ABCDEFGHIJKLMNOP

abcdefghijklmnop

HIDDEN OBJECTS

COLOR ME!

L👀k for these objects hiding in the picture. Color each object you find!

SCAVENGER COUNTING

Count the items around your house and fill in the blanks.

I have _____ **sweaters** in my closet.

I have _____ pairs of **pajamas**.

I can count _____ pairs of **shoelaces** in my closet.

Draw a line to the time of day you do each activity shown below.

10:00PM

5:30PM

7:30AM

Playing on the computer

Sleeping

Eating breakfast

What Doesn't Belong?

Draw an X on the picture that doesn't belong.

Make a Calendar:

Adult supervision is recommended.

March

Materials

scissors
glue
construction paper
pencil
red crayon
cotton balls
brown or orange yarn

March is the third month of the year. March is a good month for flying kites. It can be very windy. Weather in March can change quickly. Sometimes it is cold at the beginning of the month and warmer at the end of the month. If the weather is bad when March begins and is nice when March ends, people say that March "comes in like a lion and goes out like a lamb."

Directions

1. Cut out a copy of the calendar grid. Glue the grid to a sheet of construction paper.

2. Ask an adult what day of the week March starts on next year.

3. Number the squares from 1 to 31.

4. Write the month above the calendar grid.

5. Some calendars show holidays in red. These are some holidays you might want to put on your calendar. Passover and Easter are two holidays you might include. Some years these holidays are in March, while other years these holidays are in April. Check with an adult to find out the dates for Passover and Easter next year. Circle the dates with a red crayon. If anyone in your family has a birthday in March, add it to your red-letter days.

St. Patrick's Day	March 17
Spring begins	March 21
Birthdays and	_____
Special Events	_____
	_____

6. Decorate your calendar. You may want to make lions and lambs.

7. Cut out the lion head and mane and the lamb.

8. Trace the lion head and mane onto brown construction paper, and cut out your new lion. Glue the head to the center of the mane.

9. Glue the lion onto your calendar page. Cut yarn into strands, and glue the strands around your lion's head.

10. Draw your lion's face.

11. Glue cotton balls onto the lamb's body. Glue the lamb to your calendar page.

12. Draw your lamb's face.

Can you find...?

Circle the items hidden in the picture.

Reggie

Diggs

Tree

Summer
Vacation®
Book

Food Dish

Count the Circus Objects

Fill in the blanks with the correct number of each object.

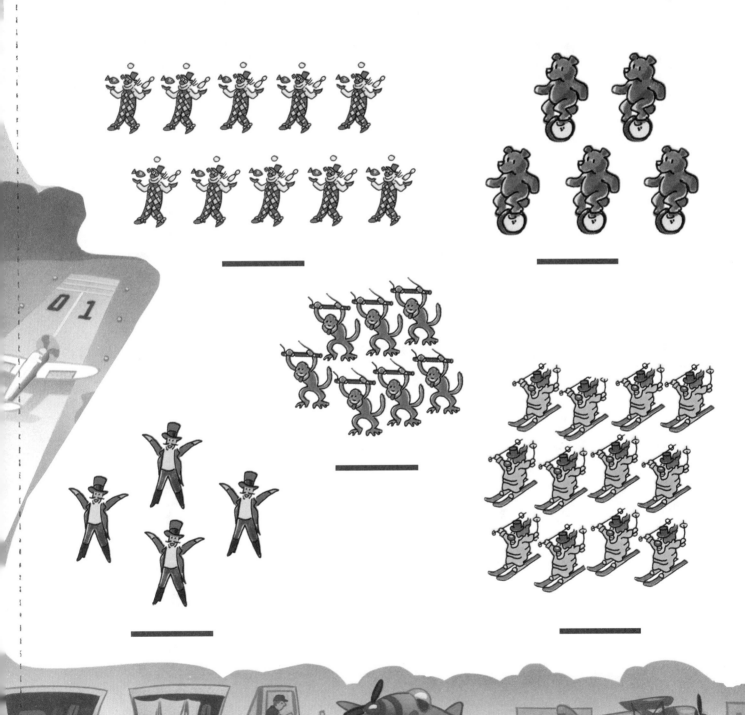

LETTER SOUNDS

Write the first letter in each picture name.

____

____

____

____

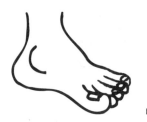
____

Alphamaze
Can you follow the E's starting from the bottom?

End

Z	A	H	E	F	K	H
F	H	E	E	Z	A	A
P	E	E	Q	A	V	H
H	E	H	G	H	W	G
L	E	E	E	D	F	A
F	P	G	E	E	K	H
C	H	K	C	E	E	E
O	F	A	H	B	F	E

ACTIVITY

Adult supervision is recommended.

Funny-Face Feet

Materials:

white construction paper

pencil

scissors

crayons or colored markers

Directions:

1. Place your foot on construction paper and draw around it.

2. Decorate the foot to look like a face.

3. Cut out around the funny face.

4. Now make a few more.

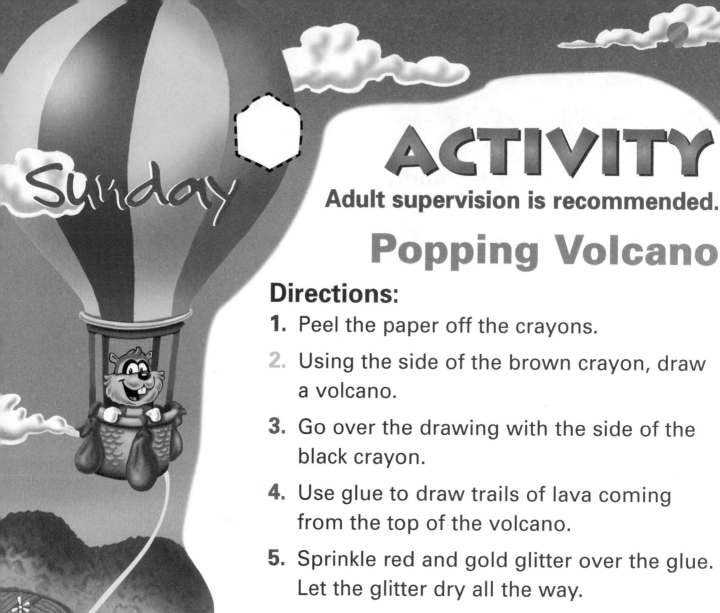

Sunday

ACTIVITY

Adult supervision is recommended.

Popping Volcano

Directions:

1. Peel the paper off the crayons.

2. Using the side of the brown crayon, draw a volcano.

3. Go over the drawing with the side of the black crayon.

4. Use glue to draw trails of lava coming from the top of the volcano.

5. Sprinkle red and gold glitter over the glue. Let the glitter dry all the way.

6. Glue popped popcorn to the top of the volcano.

7. Use a black marker to make some of the popcorn look like it's popping out.

Materials:

white construction
  paper
brown and black
  crayons
red and gold glitter
glue
popped popcorn
black marker

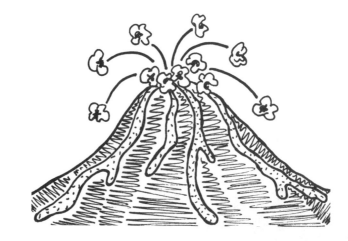

COMPLETE THE KIDS

Draw the shoes on the boy and girl.
Use our ideas or design your own.

COLOR ME!

Party at the Lake

Chapter 8: Treasure in the Grass

Ask an adult to help you read this story.

Reggie, Diggs, and Velvet kept walking.

"There is something red in the grass," said Reggie.

Velvet said, "Maybe it is a flower for the party."

Suddenly, a bird flew down. It was Rosa Robin. "Do you like my ribbon?" she asked.

Activity 1

Skill: Story Comprehension—Sequence

Circle the picture that shows what happens *first* when you have a birthday party.

"Oh, yes," said Reggie. "Can you help us decorate for the Dragonfly party?" he asked.

"Follow me," said Rosa. She took them to her nest. There were many red ribbons and pieces of paper there.

"Wonderful!" said Velvet.

Activity 2

Skill: Print Awareness—Vocabulary Recognition

Circle the picture of a *ribbon*.

Aa Bb Cc Dd Ee Ff Gg H

AQUARIUM crossword

1
1
2
2
2
3
3

Across ➡

1.

2.

3.

Down ⬇

1.

2.

HINTS: shark   water   fish   tank   eel

HIDDEN OBJECTS

COLOR ME!

L👀k for these objects hiding in the picture. Color each object you find!

SCAVENGER COUNTING

Count the items around your house and fill in the blanks.

I have _____ pairs of **socks** in my drawer.

There are _____ **shirts** in my room.

I have _____ **pockets** in my closet.

Draw a line to the time of day you do each activity shown below.

4:00PM   **7:00**PM   **10:00**AM

In school   Swimming   Putting on pajamas

What Doesn't Belong?

Draw an X on the picture that doesn't belong.

April

Make a Calendar:
Adult supervision is recommended.

Materials
scissors
glue
construction paper
pencil
red crayon
clip-type clothespin
small, sealable plastic bag
scraps of wrapping paper or tissue paper
1 brown pipe cleaner

April is the fourth month of the year. It has 30 days. In many places around the world, signs of spring start to appear. In these places, buds begin to form on trees, and bulbs peek through the soil. Caterpillars begin their change to butterflies.

Directions

1. Cut out a copy of the calendar grid. Glue the grid to a sheet of construction paper.

2. Ask an adult what day of the week April starts on next year.

3. Number the squares from 1 to 30.

4. Write the month above the calendar grid.

5. Some calendars show holidays in red. These are some holidays you might want to put on your calendar. Passover and Easter are two holidays you might include. Some years these holidays are in April, while other years these holidays are in March. Check with an adult to find out the dates for Passover and Easter next year. Circle the dates with a red crayon. If anyone in your family has a birthday in April, add it to your red-letter days.

April Fool's Day	April 1
Earth Day	April 22
Birthdays and Special Events	_____
	_____

6. Decorate your calendar. You can make a colorful butterfly.

7. Cut or tear scraps of tissue or wrapping paper.

8. Place the bits of paper in a small plastic bag, but do not fill the bag completely.

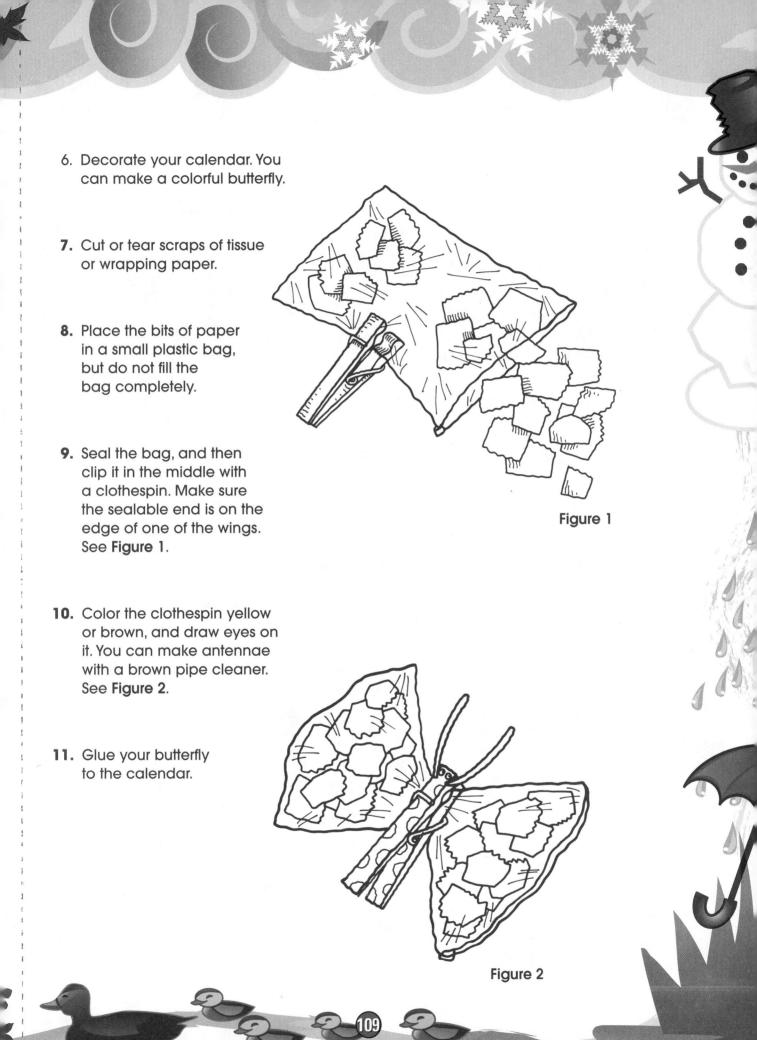

Figure 1

9. Seal the bag, and then clip it in the middle with a clothespin. Make sure the sealable end is on the edge of one of the wings. See **Figure 1**.

10. Color the clothespin yellow or brown, and draw eyes on it. You can make antennae with a brown pipe cleaner. See **Figure 2**.

11. Glue your butterfly to the calendar.

Figure 2

Can you find...? Circle the items hidden in the picture.

Reggie

Diggs

Tree

Summer Vacation® Book

Food Dish

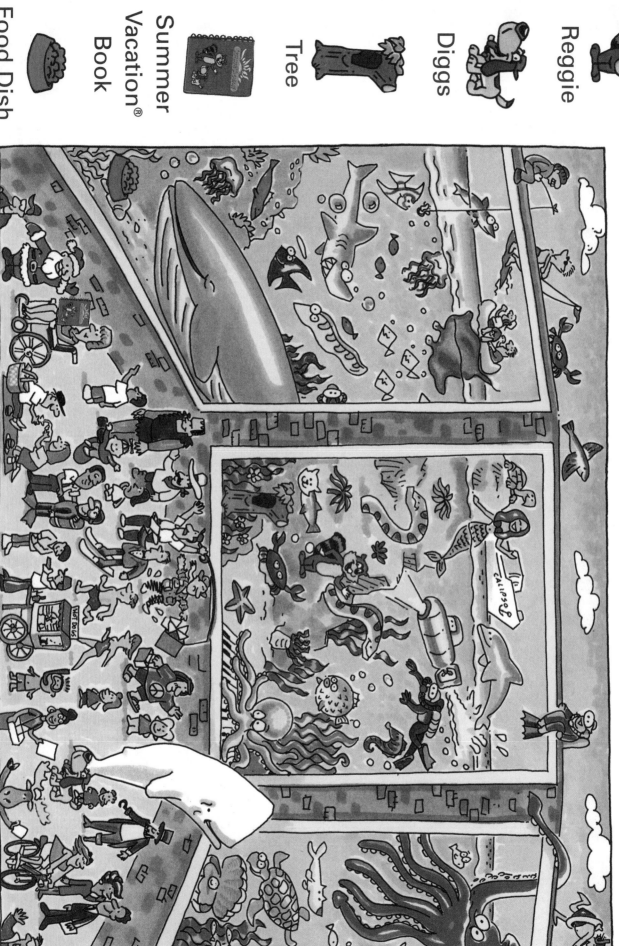

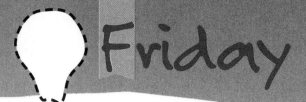

Friday

Add the groups together.

1. _____ + _____ = _____

2. _____ + _____ = _____

3. _____ + _____ = _____

4. _____ + _____ = _____

Circle the pattern that is different.

1.

2.

3.

4.

LETTER SOUNDS

Write the first letter in each picture name.

___

___

___

___

___

Alphamaze
Can you follow the C's starting from the bottom?

END

Z	A	H	C	F	K	H
F	H	V	C	C	A	A
P	N	E	Q	C	C	H
H	W	V	G	F	C	G
L	E	M	C	C	C	A
F	P	G	C	D	K	H
Y	H	C	C	A	Q	P
O	F	C	H	B	F	L

ACTIVITY

Adult supervision is recommended.

Bird in a Cage

Materials:

shoe box

white construction paper

scissors

crayons or colored markers

glue

yarn

tape

feathers (optional)

Directions:

1. Draw a bird on paper and decorate it.

2. Cut out the bird and glue it inside the shoe box.

3. Glue some feathers on the bird's tail if you like.

4. Make small cuts along the top and bottom edges of the shoe box.

5. Tape a piece of yarn to the back of the shoe box.

6. Wind the yarn around the box, making the yarn go into each little cut.

7. Tape the end of the yarn to the back of the box.

ACTIVITY

Adult supervision is recommended.

Bowling Game

Directions:

1. Cover each can with paper. Decorate them using stickers, markers, or paint.

2. Number the cans from 1 to 6. Make the numbers big and black.

3. Set the cans in three rows as shown.

4. Roll the ball into the cans.

5. Add the numbers on the fallen cans to get your score.

6. Play this with a friend.

Materials:

6 potato chip cans

paint or stickers

construction paper

colored markers

glue

scissors

small foam ball

COMPLETE THE KIDS

Draw the pajamas on the girl and boy. Use our ideas or design your own. Draw the arms if you need to.

Monday

Party at the Lake
Chapter 9: A Special Gift

Ask an adult to help you read this story.

"We must give a present to the Dragonfly family," said Reggie.

Velvet said, "I will make them curtains for their new home."

"What can we give them, Reggie?" asked Diggs.

Activity 1

Skill: Word Recognition

Find these words in the puzzle below.

nut   log   duck   lake   sun   gift

S	U	N	L	O	G
E	N	W	A	W	I
D	U	C	K	E	F
P	T	S	E	R	T

Reggie thought for a while. Then he said, "There are blackberries growing by the lake. We will make them blackberry jam."

"Oh, yes!" said Diggs. "It is good and it is sweet."

"It will taste good on a hot day," said Velvet.

Activity 2

Skill: Antonyms

**Antonyms are words that are opposites.
Sad is the opposite of *happy*. Match the words that are the opposites of each other.**

hot   good

under   cold

bad   big

little   over

PARK **crossword**

Across ➡

1.

2.

Down ⬇

1.

2.

3.

HINTS: tree   swings   run   grass   slide

HIDDEN OBJECTS

COLOR ME!

L👀k for these objects hiding in the picture. Color each object you find!

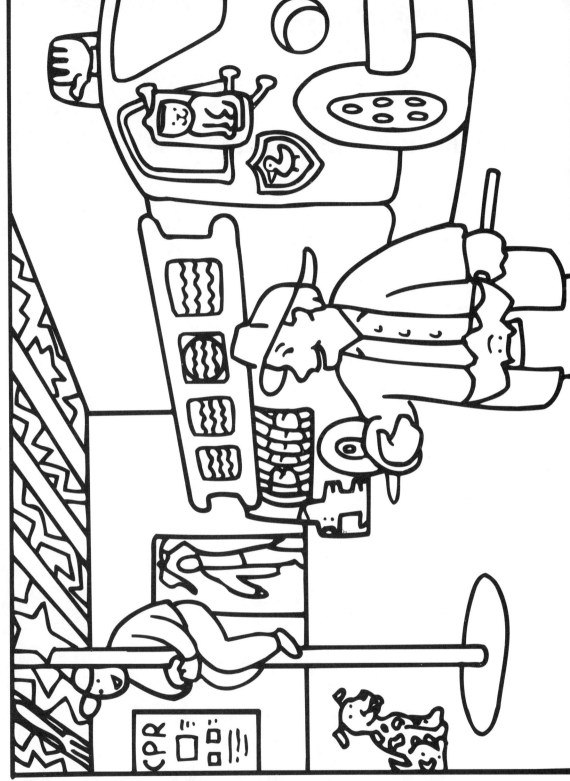

SCAVENGER COUNTING

Count the items around your house and fill in the blanks.

I have_____ pairs of **shorts**.

I can count _____ pairs of
slippers in my home.

I am wearing
_____ **snaps** today.

Draw a line to the time of day you do each activity shown below.

8:00PM

7:30AM

3:00PM

Waking up

Bedtime story

Getting off the bus

What Doesn't Belong?

Draw an X on the picture that doesn't belong.

Make a Calendar:

Adult supervision is recommended.

May

Materials

scissors
glue
construction paper
pencil
red crayon
plastic straw
tape
ruler
stapler (optional)

In May the flowers bloom again. The rains in April have helped the flowers bloom in May. Because April is so rainy in many areas, some people say, "April showers bring May flowers."

Directions

1. Cut out a copy of the calendar grid. Glue the grid to a sheet of construction paper.

2. Ask an adult what day of the week May starts on next year.

3. Number the squares from 1 to 31.

4. Write the month above the calendar grid.

5. Some calendars show holidays in red. These are some holidays you might want to put on your calendar. Circle the date with a red crayon. If anyone in your family has a birthday in May, add it to your red-letter days.

Cinco de Mayo	May 5
Mother's Day	The second Sunday in May
Victoria Day (Canada)	The Monday before May 25
Memorial Day	The last Monday in May

Birthdays and Special Events _____

_____

_____

_____

_____

6. Decorate your calendar. You might want to make May flowers.

7. Fold a sheet of construction paper in half, lengthwise.

8. Draw a line 1 in. (2.5 cm) from the open end, across the width of the paper.

9. Cut strips $\frac{1}{4}$ in. to $\frac{1}{2}$ in. (.6 cm to 1.3 cm) from the folded edge up to the line. See **Figure 1**.

Figure 1

10. Fold the two side edges together, and roll the paper lengthwise. Fasten with glue, tape, or staples.

11. Glue to the top half of your calendar page. Use a drinking straw or green construction paper for your stem. See **Figure 2**.

Figure 2

Can you find...?

Circle the items hidden in the picture.

Reggie

Diggs

Tree

Summer
Vacation®
Book

Food Dish

Search for Answers

Look at the picture on page 124 and use the word list to fill in the blanks in the sentences below. *Have an adult help you!*

birthday cake	**rocket**
ladybug	**plane**
flags	**bubbles**
moose	**licking**

1. The boy in the apple tree is reaching for a _____.

2. What kind of animal is in the pear tree? _____.

3. There are two _____ on top of the sand castle.

4. A _____ is climbing the apple tree.

5. The child next to the man with the jogging stroller is blowing _____.

6. The man with the yellow shirt and purple pants who is standing on the picnic blanket is holding a _____ _____.

7. The boy next to the park bench is _____ the girl's lollipop.

8. There is a _____ blasting off in the background.

MATCHING SOUNDS

Draw a line to the picture that starts with the letter.

V

E

R

Alphamaze

Can you follow the lowercase alphabet starting from the bottom?

END

z	y	x	V	U	T	F
L	M	w	v	u	t	s
l	m	n	o	p	q	r
k	K	H	G	F	J	R
j	i	h	g	E	D	A
O	L	H	f	e	d	c
N	M	I	G	F	B	b
K	E	D	C	B	A	a

↑

ACTIVITY

Adult supervision is recommended.

Flower Pendant

Materials:

flowers

leaves

thin cardboard

clear
  self-adhesive
  paper

glue

tape

scissors

hole punch

yarn

Directions:

1. Press some small flowers and leaves under some books for a day or two.

2. Cut a rectangle of cardboard.

3. Glue the pressed flowers to the cardboard.

4. Cover the cardboard with clear self-adhesive paper. Trim it so the edges are even.

5. Punch a hole in the top of the cardboard.

6. Tie yarn through the hole.

7. Wear your creation.

Sunday

ACTIVITY

Adult supervision is recommended.

Cookie-Saurus

Directions:

1. Draw and cut out four feet, a head, and a tail from one paper plate.

2. Fold the other paper plate in half and then open it up.

3. Place the head and tail near the fold at opposite ends of the plate and glue them in place.

4. Fold the paper plate back together and glue it around the edges.

5. Glue on the legs.

6. Decorate the dinosaur with markers or crayons.

7. To make the bony plates, glue a row of cookies along the dinosaur's back. Put glue on the flat side of the cookies. Let them dry all the way.

8. Now glue cookies on the other side of the dinosaur's back. (Do not eat glued cookies!)

Materials:

2 paper plates (thin, not heavy-duty)
glue
crayons or colored markers
pencil
scissors
small round cookies

COMPLETE THE KIDS

Draw the ears on the boy and girl.
Use our ideas or design your own.

Party at the Lake

Chapter 10: Where Is Woody?

Ask an adult to help you read this story.

At last the animals arrived at Woody Beaver's house.

"Hello!" called Reggie.

Woody did not answer.

"Where is Woody?" asked Diggs.

They looked around the house. They looked under a log.

Activity 1

Skill: Phonemic Awareness—Medial Sounds

Circle the word with the same middle sound that you hear in the middle of the word *cake*.

soon   make

give   can

They looked inside the house. They could not find Woody.

"He is lost!" cried Diggs. "I will look for him."

"We will wait here," said Velvet.

"Hurry," said Reggie. "Soon everyone will be at the lake for the party."

Activity 2

Skill: Vocabulary Comprehension—Classification

Circle the word that is a kind of *animal*.

clown   ball

duck   paint

CAMPING **crossword**

Across ➡

1.
2.
3.

Down ⬇

1.
2.
3.
4.

HINTS: **candle** **tent** **camper** **grill** **fire**

HIDDEN OBJECTS

COLOR ME!

L👀k for these objects hiding in the picture. Color each object you find!

Wednesday
SCAVENGER COUNTING

Count the items around your house and fill in the blanks.

I have _____ **bathing suits**.

Today I am wearing _____ **button(s)**.

I can count _____ **elbows** in my house.

Draw a line to the time of day you do each activity shown below.

 **12:00**PM

 **7:30**AM

 **5:00**PM

Doing homework

Eating lunch

Eating breakfast

What Doesn't Belong?

Draw an X on the picture that doesn't belong.

Make a Calendar:

Adult supervision is recommended.

June

Materials

scissors
glue
construction paper
pencil
red crayon
nontoxic washable paint
paper plate
paper towels
crayons or washable markers

> June is the sixth month of the year. School is over, and summer begins. Some people go on vacations. As you play outside, you may see many different kinds of insects and bugs. It is fun to collect fireflies on warm summer nights.

Directions

1. Cut out a copy of the calendar grid. Glue the grid to a sheet of construction paper.

2. Ask an adult what day of the week June starts on next year.

3. Number the squares from 1 to 30.

4. Write the month above your calendar grid.

5. Some calendars show holidays in red. These are some holidays you might want to put on your calendar. Circle the date with a red crayon. If anyone in your family has a birthday in June, add it to your red-letter days.

Father's Day	The third Sunday in June
Summer begins	June 21
Birthdays and Special Events	_____
	_____
	_____
	_____
	_____

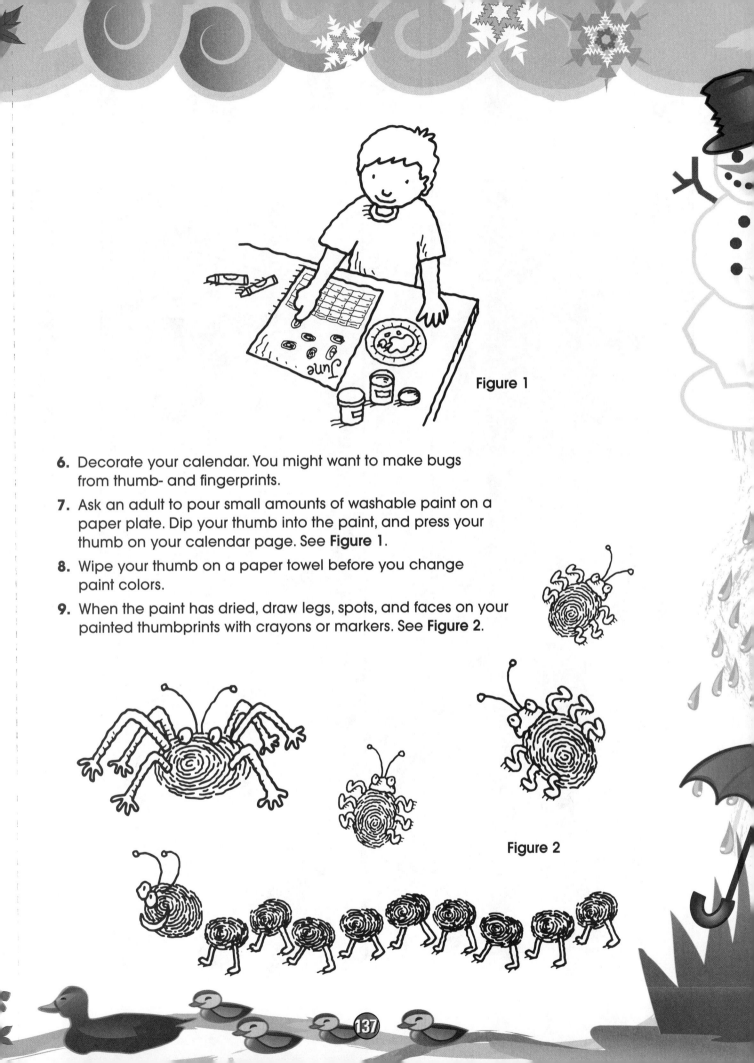

Figure 1

6. Decorate your calendar. You might want to make bugs from thumb- and fingerprints.

7. Ask an adult to pour small amounts of washable paint on a paper plate. Dip your thumb into the paint, and press your thumb on your calendar page. See **Figure 1**.

8. Wipe your thumb on a paper towel before you change paint colors.

9. When the paint has dried, draw legs, spots, and faces on your painted thumbprints with crayons or markers. See **Figure 2**.

Figure 2

Can you find...?

Circle the items hidden in the picture.

Reggie

Diggs

Tree

Summer Vacation® Book

Food Dish

Object Count

How many objects can you count?
Fill in the blanks with the correct number of each object.

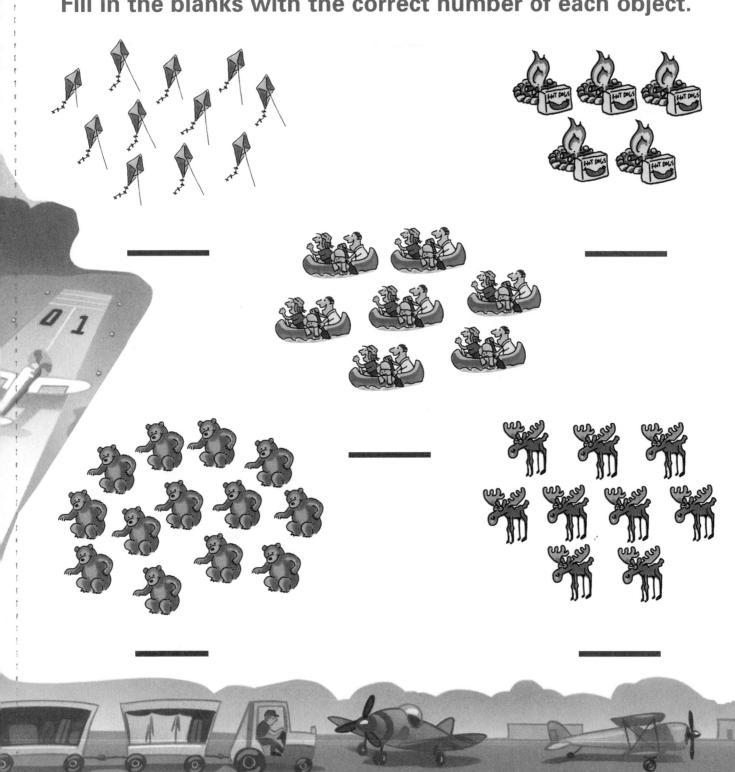

_____   _____

_____

_____   _____

Write the first letter in each picture name.

 ___

 ___

 ___

 ___

 ___

Alphamaze

Can you follow the M's starting from the bottom?

END

W	M	N	C	F	W	N
F	M	M	M	O	A	A
P	W	N	M	N	C	N
H	M	M	M	F	P	G
W	M	U	W	N	N	A
F	M	M	M	M	W	H
Y	N	N	L	M	N	P
W	W	F	C	H	M	B	L

ACTIVITY

Adult supervision is recommended.

Name Garland

Materials:

36" (91 cm)
  shoestring

3 to 4 plastic
  drinking straws

colored markers or
  crayons

scissors

stapler

ruler

construction paper

Directions:

1. Cut one 3" x 4" (8 cm x 10 cm) rectangle for each letter of your first name.

2. Snip the drinking straws into 1-inch (3 cm) lengths.

3. Fold down 1 inch (3 cm) at the top of each rectangle.

4. Staple the rectangles as shown.

5. Write one letter of your first name on each rectangle. Decorate each letter.

6. String the rectangles and the straws on the shoestring as shown.

7. Hang the finished shoestring on a wall, a bulletin board, or between two objects.

Note: If your name has more than six letters, you may need a longer shoestring. You can also use yarn instead of a shoestring.

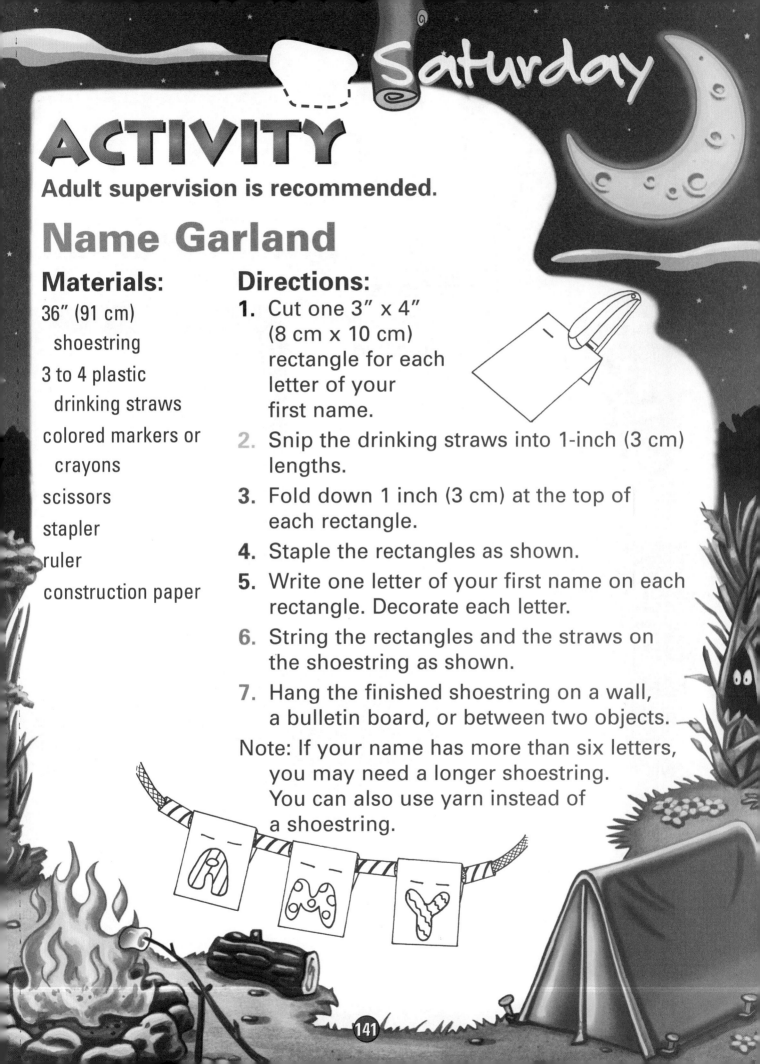

ACTIVITY

Adult supervision is recommended.

Bug on a Screen

Directions:

1. Draw and color a large bug on white construction paper.

2. Lay the netting over the paper.

3. Secure the netting by stapling it around the edges of the paper.

4. Trim the netting to match the paper.

5. Cut 1-inch (3 cm) strips of black paper.

6. Glue them to the edges of the paper to create a frame.

Materials:

construction paper—black, white

scissors

glue

crayons

stapler

black netting

COMPLETE THE KIDS

Draw a mouth on the boy and girl.
Use our ideas or come up with your own.

Monday

Party at the Lake
Chapter 11: Surprise! Surprise!

Ask an adult to help you read this story.

All the animals arrived at the party. Velvet and Reggie were very excited. They left Woody's house. They ran to the party.

Suddenly the air was filled with humming.

"It is the bees," said Velvet.

"No," said Reggie. "It is the Dragonfly family!"

"Surprise! Surprise!" cried the animals. "Welcome home!"

Activity 1

Skill: Vocabulary Recognition

Find the words about time in the puzzle below.

before   soon   now   then   when   next

X	W	N	E	X	T
C	H	O	S	A	H
B	E	F	O	R	E
R	N	P	O	L	N
G	Q	C	N	O	W

144

Just then Diggs arrived with Woody. Woody had been sleeping.

"Thank you," said Woody. "This is a nice surprise."

"The surprise is a party for the Dragonfly family," said Reggie. "Now it is a surprise for you, too!"

"This party is a surprise for everyone!" said Diggs.

Activity 2

Skill: Reading Comprehension—Character Feelings

How do Mr. and Mrs. Dragonfly probably feel about the party? Circle the picture that best shows how they *feel*.

CLASSROOM crossword

Across ➡

1.

2.

3.

Down ⬇

1.

4.

HINTS: pencil   paint   desk   paper   chalk

HIDDEN OBJECTS

L👀k for these objects hiding in the picture. Color each object you find!

SCAVENGER COUNTING

Count the items around your house and fill in the blanks.

My family has _____ **ears**.

My family has _____ **eyes**.

I can count _____ **hands** in my home.

Draw a line to the time of day you do each activity shown below.

 7:30 AM

 7:00 PM

 6:00 PM

Eating dinner

Getting dressed

Putting on pajamas

What Doesn't Belong?

Draw an X on the picture that doesn't belong.

149

Make a Calendar:
Adult supervision is recommended.

July

Materials
scissors
glue
construction paper
pencil
red crayon
paper plate
watermelon seeds or a washable marker
paintbrush or sponge cut into pieces

The seventh month of the year is July. It is a month to remember your country's freedom. Some people fly flags and set off fireworks to celebrate. July is a good month for picnics. What is your favorite picnic food?

Directions

1. Cut out a copy of the calendar grid. Glue the grid to a sheet of construction paper.

2. Ask an adult what day of the week July starts on next year.

3. Number the squares from 1 to 31.

4. Write the month above your calendar grid.

5. Some calendars show holidays in red. These are some holidays you might want to put on your calendar. Circle the date with a red crayon. If anyone in your family has a birthday in July, add it to your red-letter days.

Canada Day	July 1
Independence Day	July 4
Birthdays and Special Events	_____
	_____
	_____

6. Decorate your calendar. You might want to make a slice of watermelon or another picture of your favorite picnic food.

Figure 1

7. To make a watermelon,
   cut a paper plate in half.

8. Using a paintbrush or sponge pieces, paint the edge
   green for the rind of your watermelon.

9. Then, paint the rest of the plate pink.

10. When dry, glue, draw, or paint watermelon seeds onto the
    pink part of your plate. See **Figure 1**.

11. Glue your watermelon to your calendar page. See **Figure 2**.

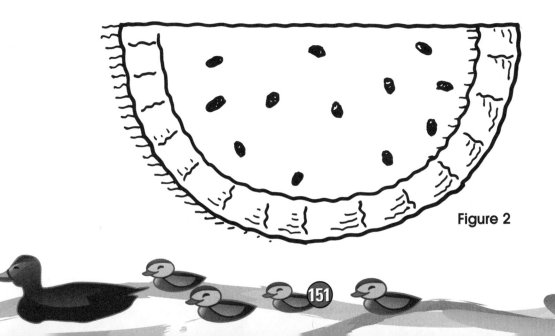

Figure 2

Can you find...?

Circle the items hidden in the picture.

Reggie

Diggs

Tree

Summer Vacation® Book

Food Dish

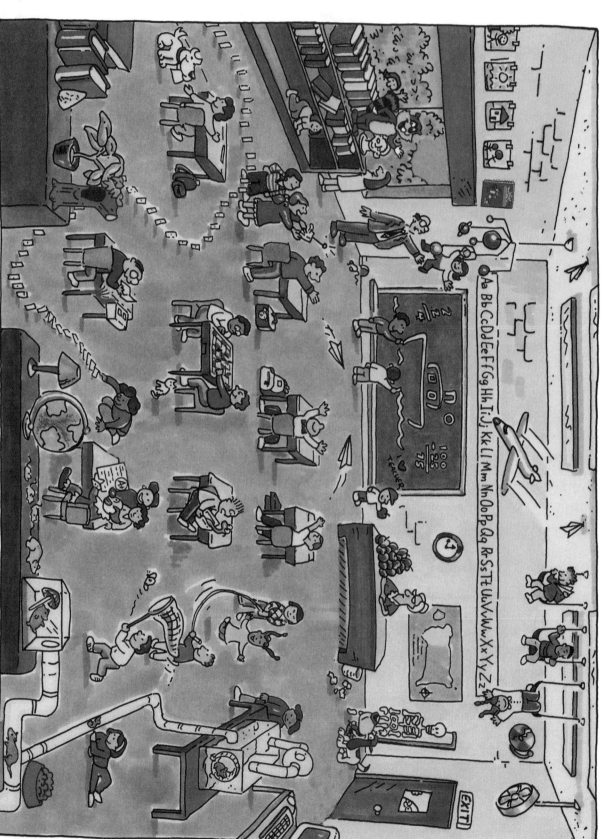

Add the groups together.

1. _____ + _____ = _____

2. _____ + _____ = _____

3. _____ + _____ = _____

4. _____ + _____ = _____

Circle the pattern that is different.

1.

2.

3.

4.

Draw a line to the picture
that starts with the letter.

B

Q

A

Alphamaze

End

Can you count to 14 starting
from the bottom?

4	3	14	4	7	3	13
6	12	13	1	10	6	1
1	11	7	3	7	8	2
9	10	13	1	8	9	3
8	2	4	7	11	6	12
7	6	5	4	8	3	2
2	1	2	3	11	8	13
3	4	1	5	9	6	14

ACTIVITY

Adult supervision is recommended.

Pencil Gripper

Materials:

new pencil

snap-type
  clothespin

craft or carpenter's
  glue

Directions:

1. Sharpen the pencil.

2. Spread glue on the flat surface of the clothespin.

3. Lay the pencil on the glue. Position the pencil so the end of the clothespin is just under the metal band of the pencil eraser.

4. Let it dry for a day or two.

5. Use your pencil gripper in your pocket or to keep a pencil in a handy spot.

6. When the pencil gets too short, make a new pencil gripper.

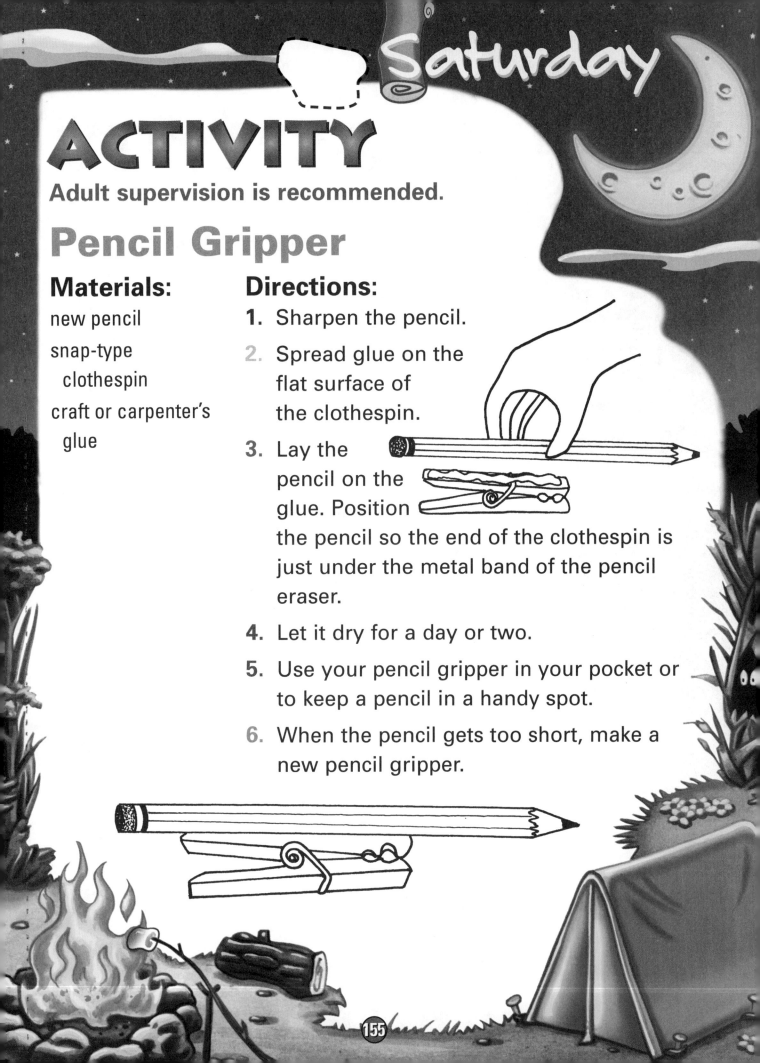

ACTIVITY

Adult supervision is recommended.

Plaid Flower

Directions:

1. Color stripes of yellow, red, and blue across the paper.

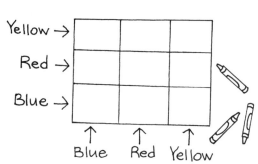

Yellow →
Red →
Blue →

↑ ↑ ↑
Blue Red Yellow

2. Now color stripes of blue, red, and yellow the other way.

3. Cut out the nine squares of color.

4. Arrange them on another paper to form a flower.

5. Add a stem, leaves and some dots to the center of the flower.

Materials:

crayons
white construction
  paper
glue
scissors

COMPLETE THE KIDS

Draw a coat on the kids.
Use our ideas or come up with your own.

Monday

Party at the Lake
Chapter 12: Music! Music! Music!

Ask an adult to help you read this story.

"We did not get to decorate," said Velvet.

"It does not matter," said Reggie. "We have lots of presents."

"And we have music," said Diggs.

"Thump! Thump!" Woody Beaver flapped his tail like a drum.

Activity 1

Skill: Reading Comprehension—Main Idea and Details

Circle the picture of the musical instrument Woody Beaver sounds like.

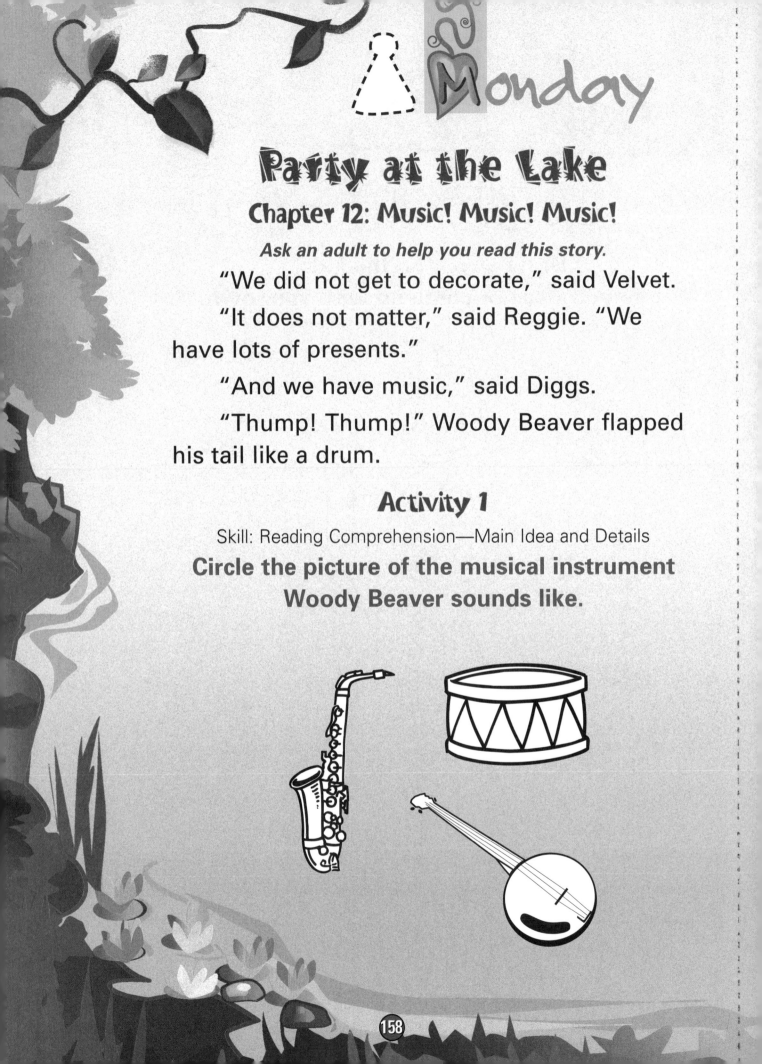

"Quack! Quack!" sang the ducks.

"Buzz! Buzz!" buzzed the bees.

"Ribbet! Ribbet!" sang the frogs.

Diggs began to howl.

"This is the most musical lake around!" said Reggie.

"And this is the best welcome home party ever!" said the Dragonfly family.

Activity 2

Skill: Reading Comprehension—Personal Response

Draw a picture of the party at the lake.

SCHOOLYARD crossword

Across ➡

1.

2.

3.

Down ⬇

1.

2.

HINTS: games   fence   girls   boys   ball

HIDDEN OBJECTS

Look for these objects hiding in the picture. Color each object you find!

COLOR ME!

SCAVENGER COUNTING

Count the items around your house and fill in the blanks.

I can count _____ **noses** in my house.

I have _____ **toes**.

There are _____ **mouths** in my home.

Draw a line to the time of day you do each activity shown below.

6:00PM

8:00AM

1:00PM

Getting on the bus

Playing at recess

Eating dinner

What Doesn't Belong?

Draw an X on the picture that doesn't belong.

Make a Calendar:

Adult supervision is recommended.

August

Materials

scissors
glue
construction paper
pencil
red crayon

August is the eighth month of the year. It is often hot in August. Many people go to the beach or shore in August. Others enjoy lazy days fishing at a lake.

Directions

1. Cut out a copy of the calendar grid. Glue the grid to a sheet of construction paper.

2. Ask an adult what day of the week August starts on next year.

3. Number the squares from 1 to 31.

4. Write the month above your calendar grid.

5. Some calendars show holidays in red. This is a holiday you might want to put on your calendar. Circle the date with a red crayon. If anyone in your family has a birthday in August, add it to your red-letter days.

August 1   Friendship Day

Birthdays and   _____

Special Events   _____

                 _____

6. Decorate your calendar. You might want to make a fishing scene.

7. Cut out the fish pattern on this page. Color the fish, or trace the fish onto construction paper. Cut out the fish made from construction paper.

8. Trace the wave pattern on this page onto blue construction paper. Cut the paper to show the waves.

9. Glue the waves and fish to the top of your calendar page.

Can you find...?

Circle the items hidden in the picture.

Reggie

Diggs

Tree

Summer Vacation® Book

Food Dish

Object Count

How many objects can you count?
Fill in the blanks with the correct number of each object.

_____   _____

_____

_____   _____

LETTER SOUNDS

Write the first letter in each picture name.

 ___

 ___

 ___

 ___

 ___

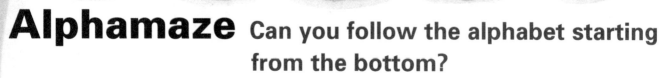

Alphamaze

Can you follow the alphabet starting from the bottom?

H	L	Q	J	V	Y	Z	End
S	W	Z	S	C	X	S	
H	G	C	D	F	W	M	
A	J	K	L	M	V	D	
F	I	H	G	N	U	T	
K	T	R	F	O	D	S	
B	C	D	E	P	Q	R	
A	L	B	G	A	B	C	

ACTIVITY

Adult supervision is recommended.

Toy Organizer

Materials:

cardboard box

construction paper

stickers or colored
  markers

scissors

glue

hole punch

Directions:

1. Cover the sides of a box with paper.

2. Decorate the paper with markers or stickers.

3. Cut a strip of paper the length of one edge of the box.

4. Glue it to the edge of the box and fold it so it hangs down over the edge.

5. Punch holes in this paper to make it look like lace or decorate it with markers.

6. Set your toys or books in the finished box.

ACTIVITY

Adult supervision is recommended.

Newspaper Fish

Directions:

1. Put two pieces of newspaper together.

2. Draw and cut out the body of a fish.

3. Cut a tail and some fins from the edge of a paper plate.

4. Glue the tail and the top and bottom fins in place.

5. Crumple some small squares of newspaper.

6. Glue them to the body.

7. Now glue the two body pieces together.

8. Glue fins to the sides of the fish.

9. When the fish is dry, decorate it with colored markers.

Materials:

newspaper
paper plate (thin, not heavy-duty)
scissors
glue
pencil
colored markers

COMPLETE THE KIDS

Draw some eyebrows on the boy and girl.
Use our ideas or design your own.

Answers

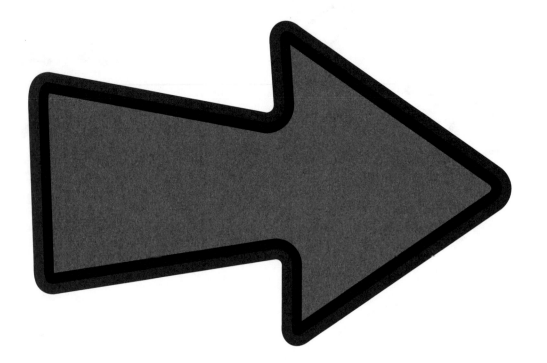

Pages 4 - 17

Week 1

MONDAY   Page 4

Circle the Different Picture

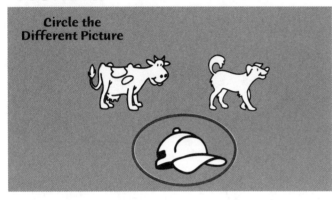

MONDAY   Page 5

Circle the Correct Day

TUESDAY   Page 6

Crossword

				2					
	1			W				4	
1	S	T	A	R	F	I	S	H	H
	A			V				H	
	N			E		3		E	
	D					F		L	
			2	B	A	L	L	L	
						N			

TUESDAY   Hidden Objects   Page 7

WEDNESDAY   Page 9

Getting up — 7 a.m.
Sleeping — 10 p.m.
Playing Soccer — 4 p.m.

What Doesn't Belong?

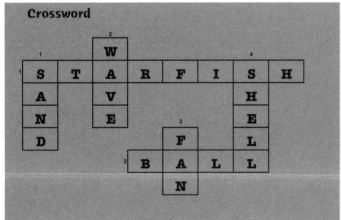

FRIDAY   Can You Find...?   Page 12

FRIDAY   Page 13

Add the Groups Together

1. 4 + 3 = 7
2. 5 + 2 = 7
3. 2 + 4 = 6
4. 3 + 3 = 6

Which Pattern is Different?

#3 is different.

MONDAY   Page 18

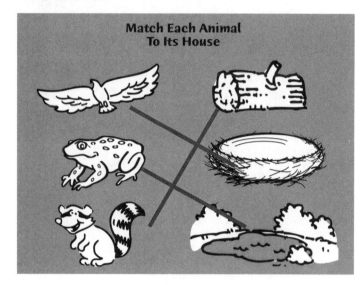

Match Each Animal To Its House

SATURDAY   Page 14

Matching Sounds

R
I
F

MONDAY   Page 19

Circle the Picture of the Word That Sounds Like House.

SATURDAY   Page 14

Maze

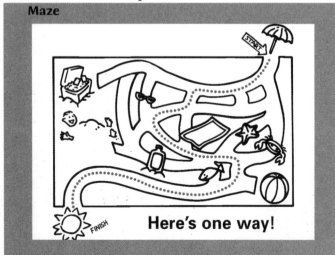

Here's one way!

TUESDAY   Page 20

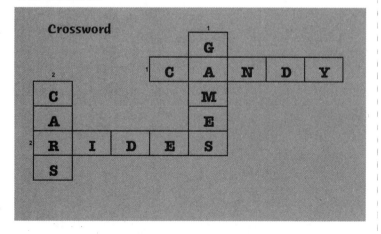

Crossword

Week 2

FRIDAY   Page 27

Search for Answers

1. Diggs
2. banana
3. purple, yellow
4. three
5. tickets
6. birds
7. balloons
8. dart board

TUESDAY   Hidden Objects   Page 21

WEDNESDAY   Page 23

Getting off the bus — 3 p.m.
Bedtime story — 8 p.m.
Eating lunch — 12 p.m.

What Doesn't Belong?

SATURDAY   Page 28

Matching Sounds

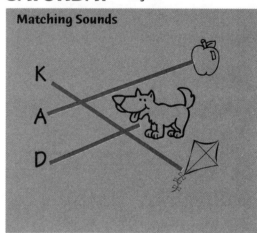

K
A
D

FRIDAY   Can You Find...?   Page 26

SATURDAY   Page 28

Maze

Here's one way!

Pages 32 - 45

Week 3

MONDAY   Page 32

Crossword

TUESDAY   Hidden Objects   Page 35

MONDAY   Page 32

Circle the Duck

WEDNESDAY   Page 37

Eating breakfast — 7:30 a.m.

In school — 10 a.m.

Doing homework — 5 p.m.

What Doesn't Belong?

TUESDAY   Page 34

Crossword

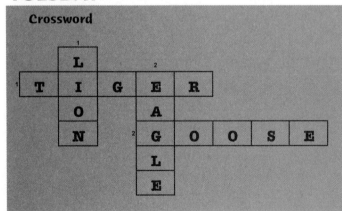

FRIDAY   Can You Find...?   Page 40

Week 3 continued

Week 4

FRIDAY Page 41

Count the Animals

There are
- 5 zebras,
- 3 penguins,
- 8 lions,
- 10 alligators,
- 1 rhinoceros,
- 2 elephants,
- 6 flamingos

MONDAY Page 46

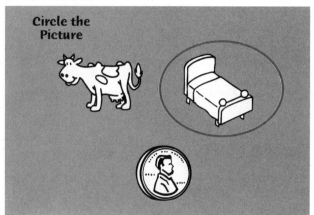

Circle the Picture

SATURDAY Page 42

Letter Sounds

= D

= B

= T

= A

= B

MONDAY Page 47

Circle the Picture

SATURDAY Page 42

Maze

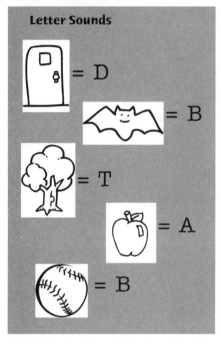

TUESDAY Page 48

Crossword

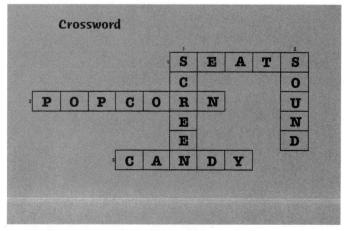

continued

Week 4

TUESDAY
Hidden Objects Page 49

WEDNESDAY Page 51

Riding a bike — 4 p.m.
Playing at recess — 1 p.m.
Getting dressed — 7:30 a.m.

What Doesn't Belong?

FRIDAY **Can You Find...?** Page 54

FRIDAY Page 55

Add the Groups Together

1. 7 + 1 = 8
2. 5 + 3 = 8
3. 8 + 2 = 10
4. 4 + 5 = 9

Which Pattern is Different?

#2 is different.

SATURDAY Page 56

Letter Sounds

 = M

 = S

 = C

 = E

 = C

SATURDAY Page 56

Maze

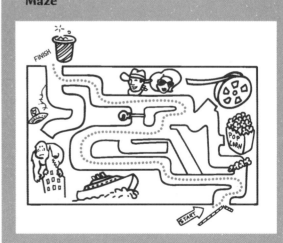

Week 5

MONDAY
Page 60

Circle the Picture

MONDAY
Page 61

Circle the Picture

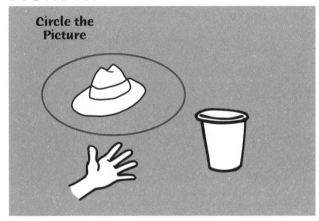

TUESDAY
Page 62

Crossword

	2				1			
	S		1 S	W	I	M
	L			A		
	I			T		
2	D	I	V	E		
	E		3	R	A	F	T

TUESDAY
Hidden Objects   Page 63

WEDNESDAY
Page 65

Playing with friends — 4 p.m.
Stargazing — 11 p.m.
Waking up — 7 a.m.

What Doesn't Belong?

FRIDAY
Can You Find...? Page 68

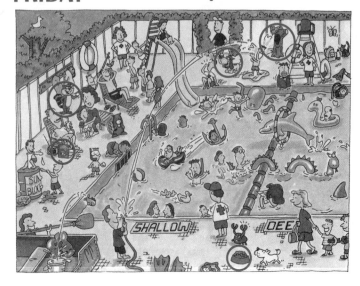

FRIDAY Page 69

Search for Answers

1. three
2. fish
3. radio
4. yellow, shallow
5. squirting
6. four
7. fence
8. shivering

MONDAY Page 74

Circle the Picture

SATURDAY Page 70

Matching Sounds

MONDAY Page 75

Circle the Word

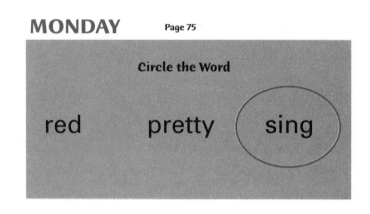

red   pretty   sing

SATURDAY Page 70

Maze

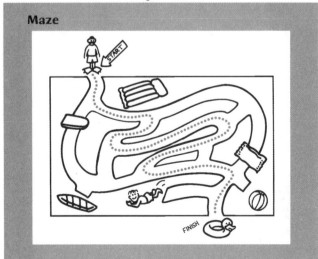

TUESDAY Page 76

Crossword

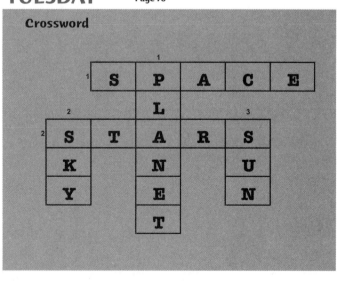

continued
Week 6

TUESDAY
Hidden Objects — Page 77

WEDNESDAY — Page 79

Getting on the bus — 8 a.m.
Playing at recess — 1 p.m.
Taking a bath — 7 p.m.

What Doesn't Belong?

FRIDAY — Can You Find...? — Page 82

FRIDAY — Page 83
Object Count

= 7

= 11

= 9

= 10

SATURDAY — Page 84
Letter Sounds

= G

= O

= B

= Z

= L

SATURDAY — Page 84

Maze

Week 7

Pages 88 - 101

MONDAY
Page 88

Circle the Picture

MONDAY
Page 89

Circle the Picture

TUESDAY
Page 90

Crossword

TUESDAY
Hidden Objects Page 91

WEDNESDAY
Page 93

Playing on the computer — 5:30 p.m.

Sleeping — 10 p.m.

Eating breakfast — 7:30 a.m.

What Doesn't Belong?

FRIDAY
Can You Find...? Page 96

continued

Week 7

FRIDAY   Page 97

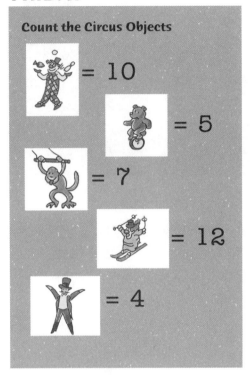

Count the Circus Objects

= 10

= 5

= 7

= 12

= 4

SATURDAY   Page 98

Letter Sounds

 = T

= B

 = U

= P

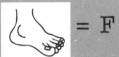 = F

SATURDAY   Page 98

Maze

			E			
		E	E			
	E	E				
	E					
	E	E	E			
			E	E		
				E	E	E
						E

Pages 102 - 115

Week 8

MONDAY   Page 102

Circle the Picture

Page 103

MONDAY

Circle the Picture

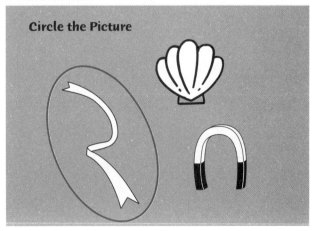

Week 8

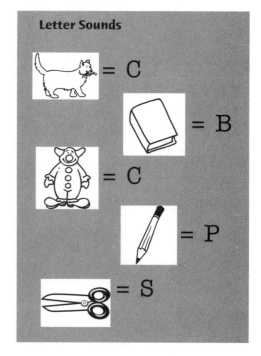

TUESDAY   Page 104

Crossword

			1	
1 F	I	S	H	
			H	
	2		A	
	W		R	
2 T	A	N	K	
	T			
	3 E	E	L	
	R			

TUESDAY   Hidden Objects   Page 105

WEDNESDAY   Page 107

In school — 10 a.m.
Swimming — 4 p.m.
Putting on pajamas — 7 p.m.

What Doesn't Belong?

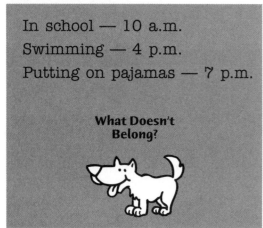

FRIDAY   Page 111

Add the Groups Together

1. 9 + 1 = 10
2. 2 + 7 = 9
3. 4 + 4 = 8
4. 3 + 7 = 10

Which Pattern is Different?

#4 is different.

SATURDAY   Page 112

Letter Sounds

= C

= B

= C

= P

= S

Week 8 continued

Pages 116 - 129

Week 9

SATURDAY   Page 112

Maze

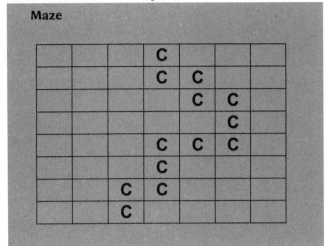

MONDAY   Page 116

Find the Words

S	U	N	L	O	G
E	N	W	A	W	I
D	U	C	K	E	F
P	T	S	E	R	T

MONDAY   Page 117

Match the Antonyms

hot — cold
under — over
bad — good
little — big

TUESDAY   Page 118

Crossword

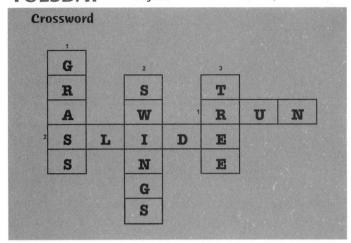

TUESDAY   Hidden Objects   Page 119

WEDNESDAY   Page 121

Waking up — 7:30 a.m.
Bedtime story — 8 p.m.
Getting off the bus — 3 p.m.

What Doesn't Belong?

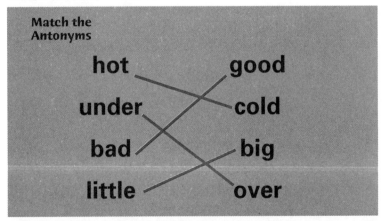

continued

Week 9

Maze

z	y	x				
		w	v	u	t	s
l	m	n	o	p	q	r
k						
j	i	h	g			
			f	e	d	c
						b
						a

FRIDAY   Can You Find...?   Page 124

Week 10

FRIDAY   Page 125

Search for Answers

1. plane
2. moose
3. flags
4. ladybug
5. bubbles
6. birthday cake
7. licking
8. rocket

MONDAY   Page 130

Circle the Word

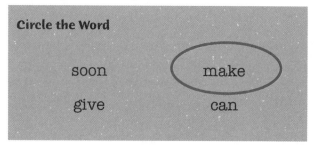

soon   make

give   can

SATURDAY   Page 126

Matching Sounds

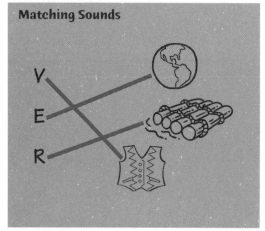

MONDAY   Page 131

Circle the Word

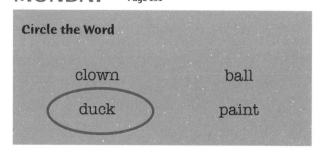

clown   ball

duck   paint

TUESDAY   Page 132

Crossword

```
                              4
                              F
            1                 I
          1 C  A  M  P  E  R  R
            A                 E
        2 T  E  N  T
            N
            D
        3 G  R  I  L  L
            E
```

FRIDAY   Can You Find...?   Page 138

MARSHMALLOWS NOW BEING SERVED

TUESDAY   Hidden Objects   Page 133

FRIDAY   Page 139

Object Count

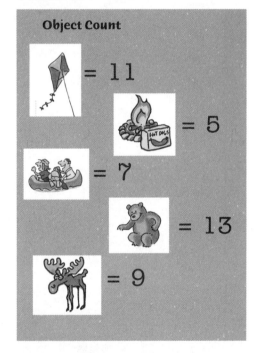

= 11

= 5

= 7

= 13

= 9

WEDNESDAY   Page 135

Doing homework — 5 p.m.

Eating lunch — 12 p.m.

Eating breakfast — 7:30 a.m.

What Doesn't Belong?

SATURDAY   Page 140

Letter Sounds

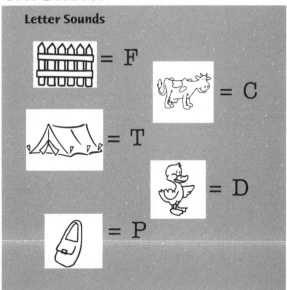

= F

= C

= T

= D

= P

Week 10 continued

SATURDAY Page 140

Maze

	M				
	M	M	M		
			M		
	M	M	M		
	M				
	M	M	M	M	
				M	
				M	

Pages 144 - 157

Week 11

MONDAY Page 144

Find the Words

X	W	N	E	X	T
C	H	O	S	A	H
B	E	F	O	R	E
R	N	P	O	L	N
G	Q	C	N	O	W

MONDAY Page 145

Circle the Face

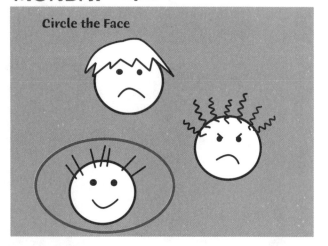

TUESDAY Page 146

Crossword

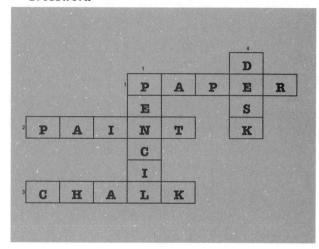

TUESDAY Hidden Objects Page 147

WEDNESDAY Page 149

Eating dinner — 6 p.m.
Getting dressed — 7:30 a.m.
Putting on pajamas — 7 p.m.

What Doesn't Belong?

Week 11

SATURDAY   Page 154
Maze

		14			
	12	13			
	11				
9	10				
8					
7	6	5	4		
		2	3		
		1			

FRIDAY   Can You Find...?   Page 152

Pages 158 - 171

Week 12

FRIDAY   Page 153

Add the Groups
Together
1. 9 + 2 = 11
2. 6 + 3 = 9
3. 6 + 5 = 11
4. 1 + 10 = 11

Which Pattern
is Different?

#2 is different.

MONDAY   Page 158

Circle the Picture

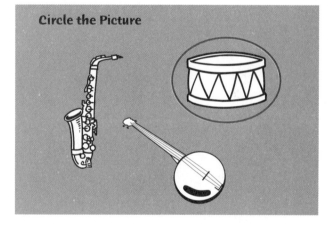

SATURDAY   Page 154

Matching Sounds

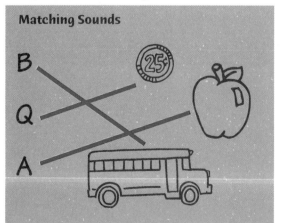

TUESDAY   Page 160

Crossword

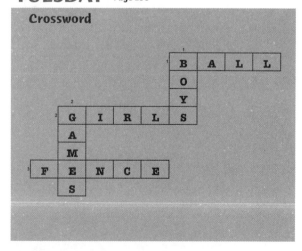

continued

Week 12

TUESDAY **Hidden Objects** Page 161

WEDNESDAY Page 163

Getting on the bus — 8 a.m.

Playing at recess — 1 p.m.

Eating dinner — 6 p.m.

What Doesn't Belong?

FRIDAY **Can You Find...?** Page 166

FRIDAY Page 167

Object Count

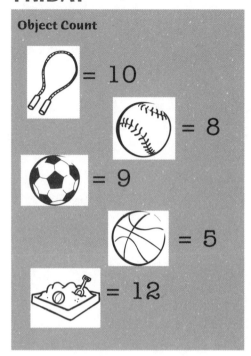

= 10

= 8

= 9

= 5

= 12

SATURDAY Page 168

Letter Sounds

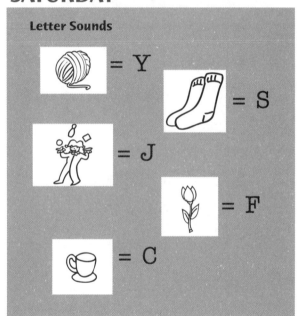

= Y

= S

= J

= F

= C

SATURDAY Page 168

Maze

					Y	Z
					X	
					W	
	J	K	L	M	V	
	I	H	G	N	U	T
			F	O		S
B	C	D	E	P	Q	R
A						

Draw a picture of yourself

Draw a picture of your family